CONTENTS

GRADE 1

CHAPTER 1 • Understanding Numbers to 10

CHAPTER 2 • Adding Facts to 5

CHAPTER 3 • Subtracting Facts to 5

CHAPTER 4 • Adding Facts to 10

CHAPTER 5 • Subtracting Facts to 10

CHAPTER 6 • Understanding Numbers to 99

CHAPTER 7 • Money

CHAPTER 8 • Measurement

CHAPTER 9 • Adding and Subtracting Facts to 12

CHAPTER 10 • Time

CHAPTER 11 • Geometry and Fractions

CHAPTER 12 • Adding and Subtracting Facts to 18

CHAPTER 13 • Adding and Subtracting 2-Digit Numbers

Name

FIVE AND ZERO

Write the number.

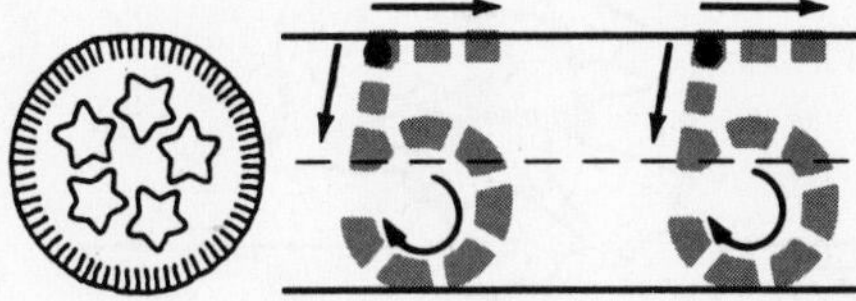

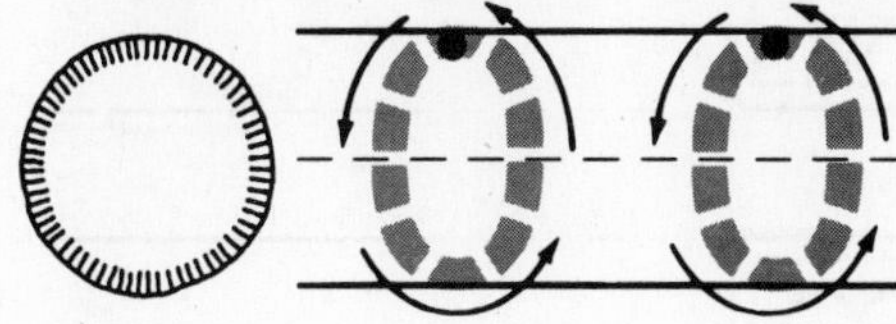

Match.

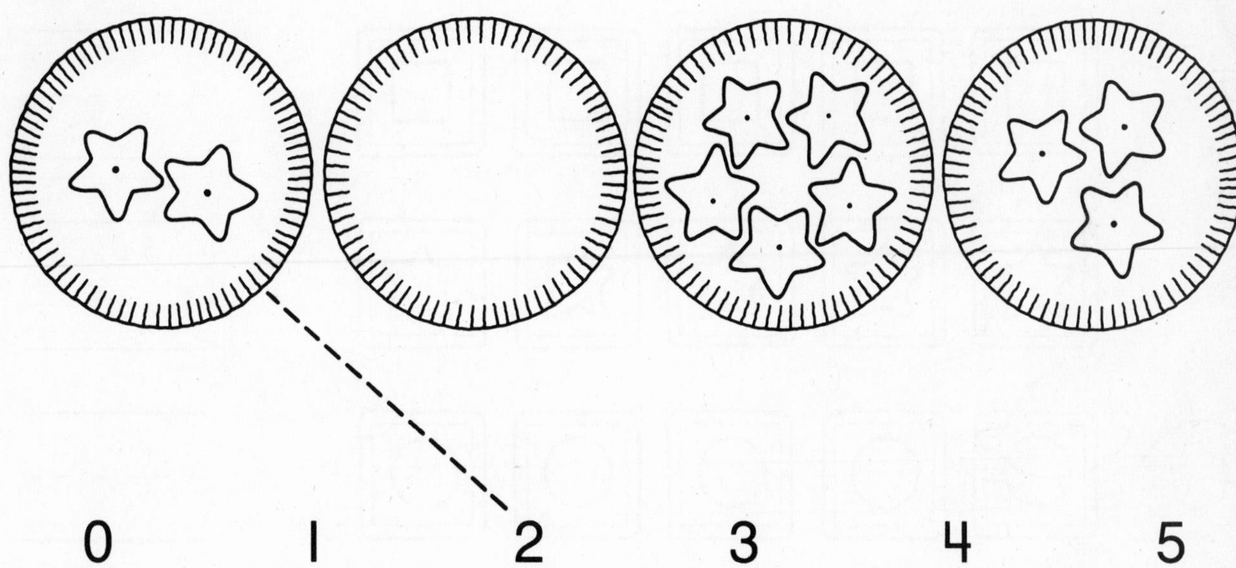

0 1 2 3 4 5

Macmillan/McGraw-Hill, MATHEMATICS IN ACTION
Grade 1, Chapter 1, Lesson 4, pages 15–16

Name

ORDER 0–5

Color to show how many.
Write the numbers.

   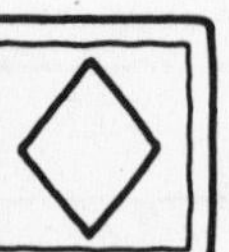   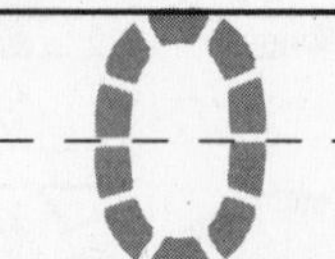

1     

2     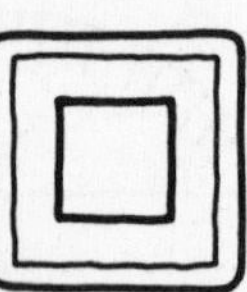

3     

4      

5     

Write the numbers in order.

Name

PROBLEM SOLVING: USING INFORMATION FROM A PICTURE

How many of each?

Write how many.

1. 3 ______ 

2. ______ 

3. ______

4. ______ 

5. ______

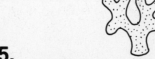

Name

Six and seven

Write the number.

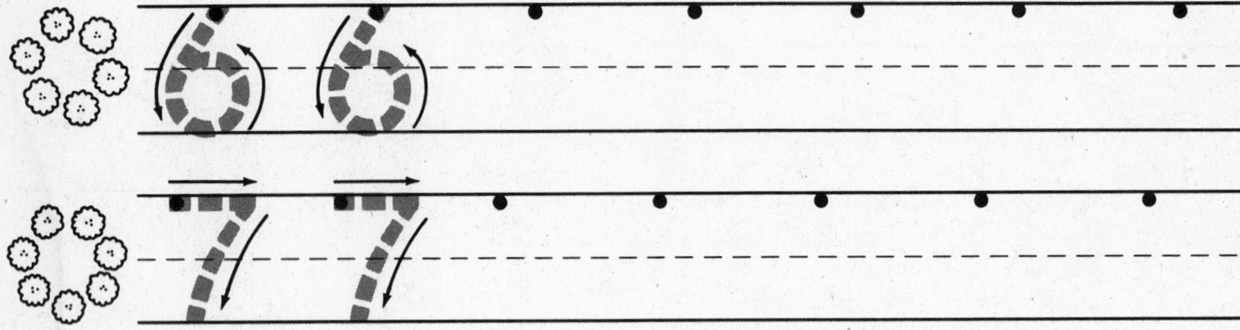

Count the dots. Color.

4 red
5 brown
6 orange
7 yellow

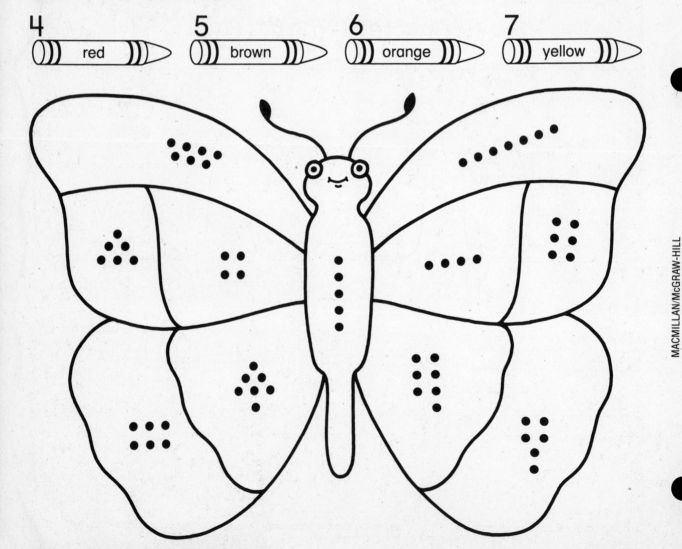

MACMILLAN/McGRAW-HILL

Name

EIGHT AND NINE

Write the number.

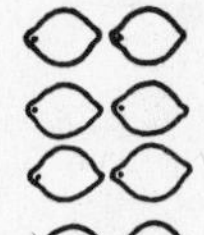
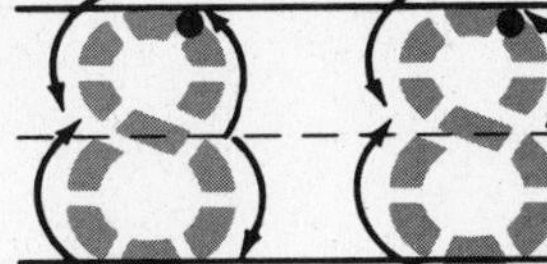

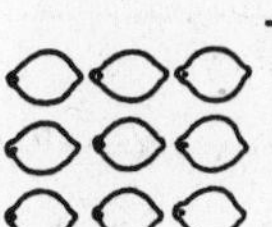
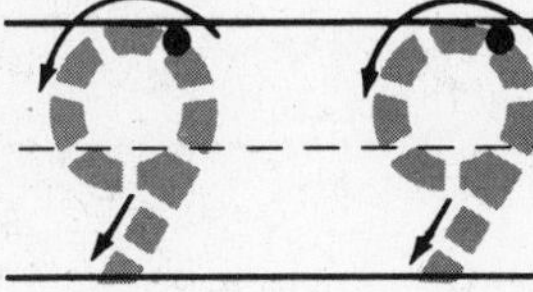

Write how many.

Macmillan/McGraw-Hill, MATHEMATICS IN ACTION
Grade 1, Chapter 1, Lesson 9, pages 25–26

Name

TEN

Write the number.

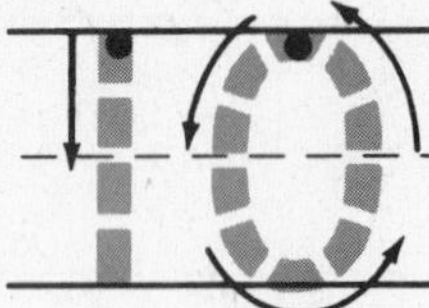

Write how many cents.

5 ¢

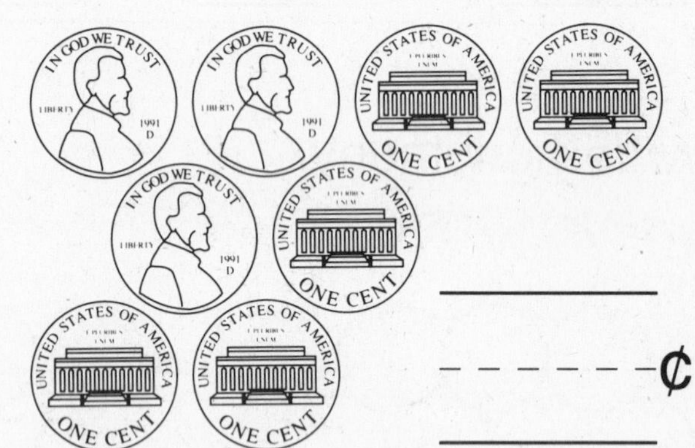

¢

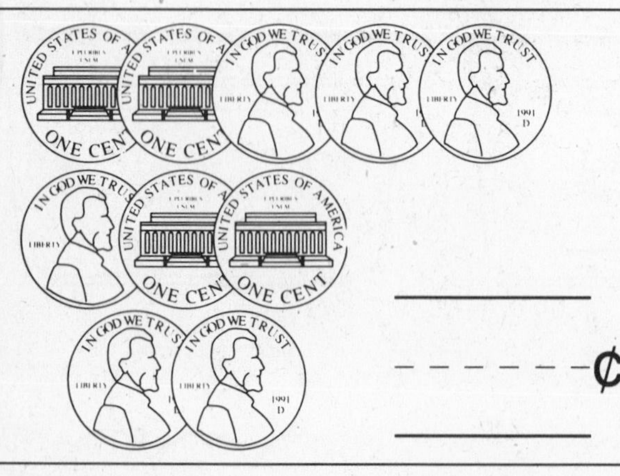

¢

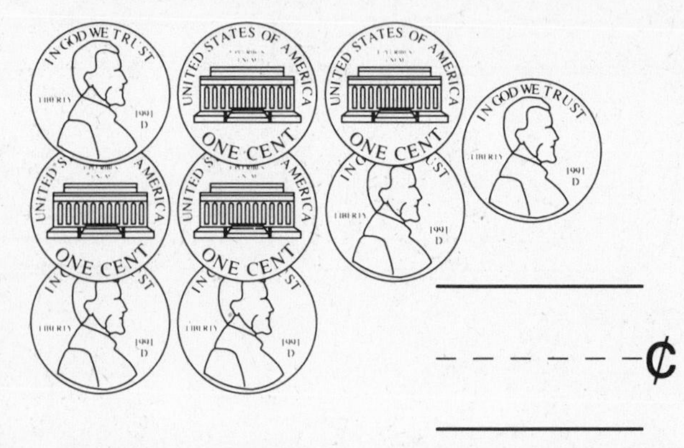

¢

¢

¢

Name

ORDER 0–10

Write the numbers in order.

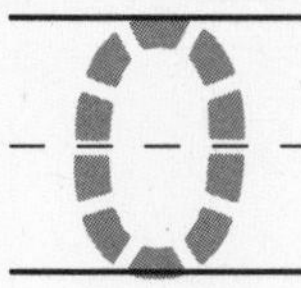
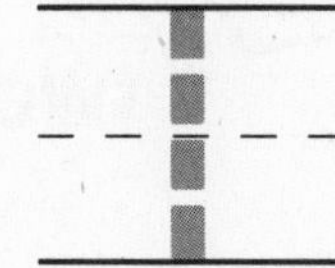

Connect the dots in order.

Start 0

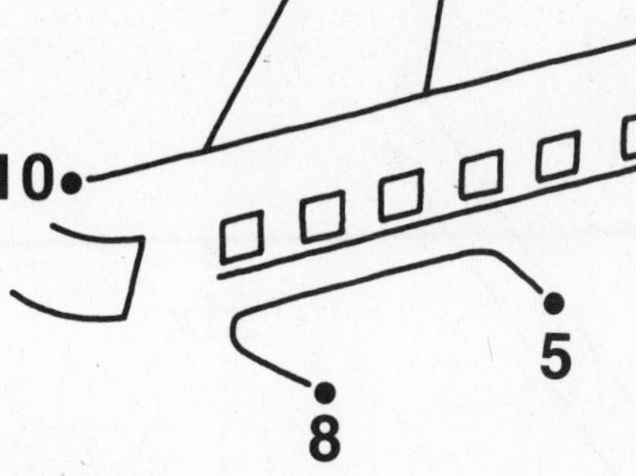
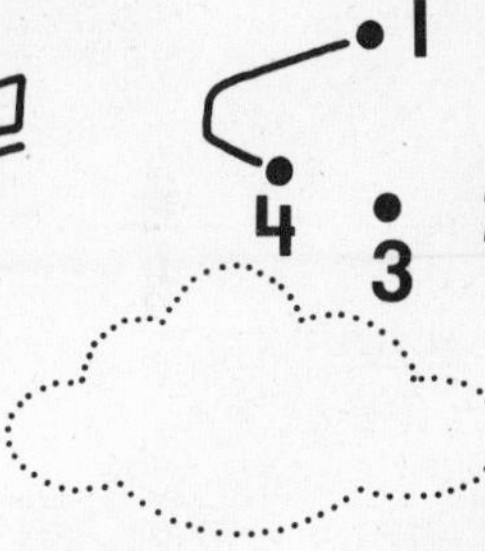

1 2 3 4 5 6 7 8 9 10

Start 0

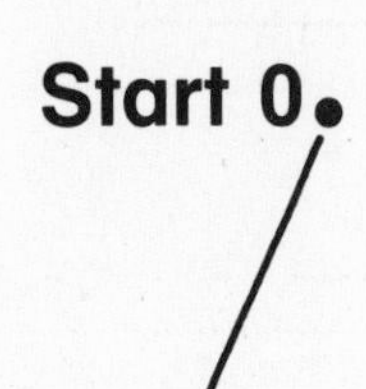

1 2 3 4 5 6 7 8 9 10

Name

NUMBER WORDS TO TEN

Connect the dots.

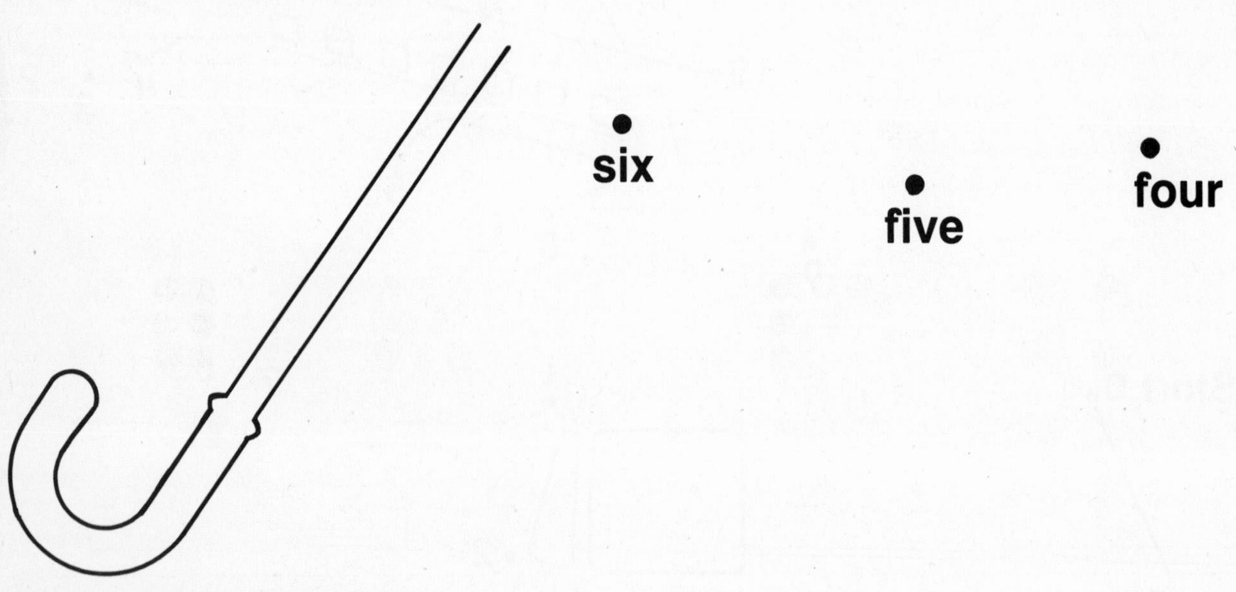

Write the numbers.

four	seven	three	nine	eight	five

Name

GREATER AND LESS

Write how many.
Ring the number that is greater.

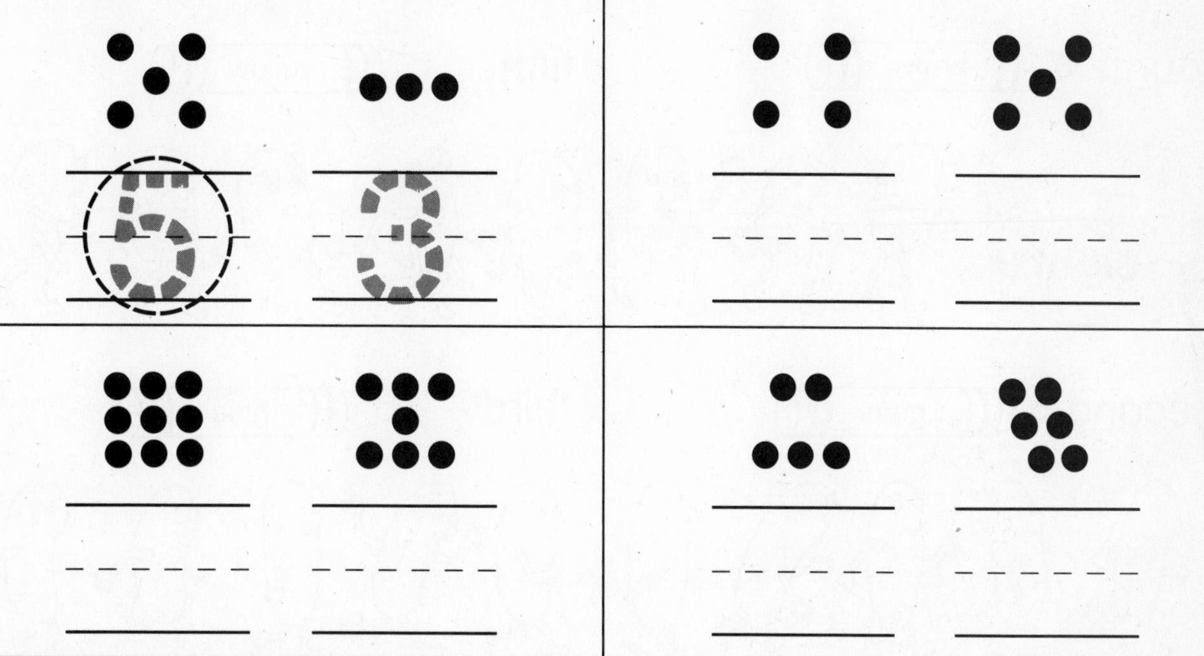

Write how many.
Ring the number that is less.

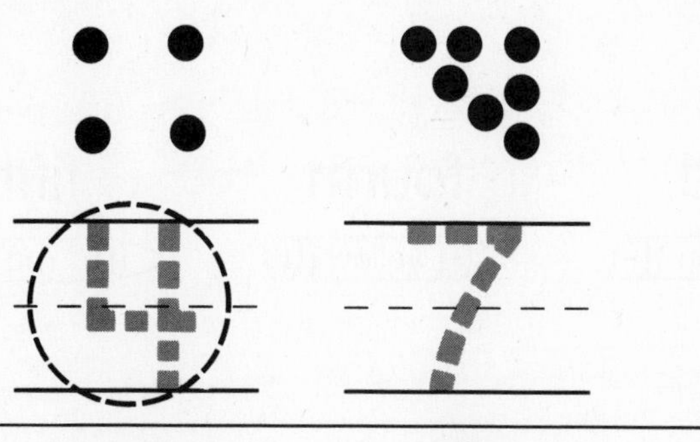

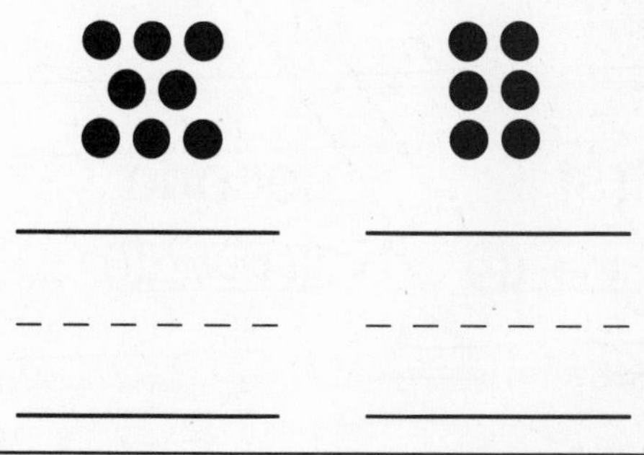

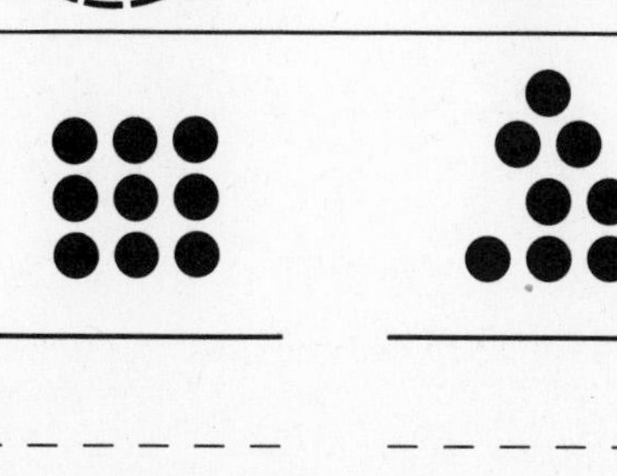

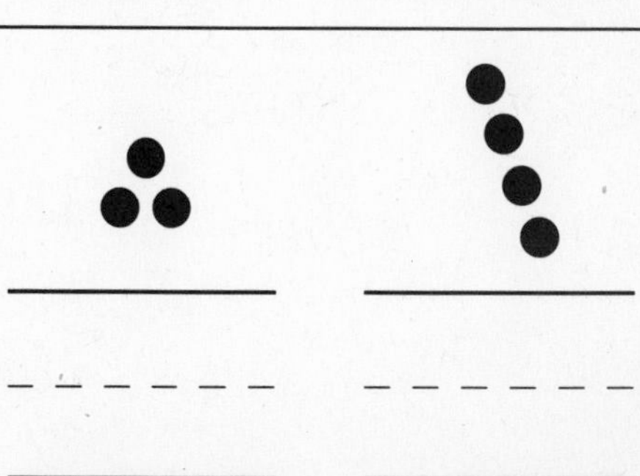

Name

ORDINAL NUMBERS

Start at the left.
Color.

fourth brown fifth yellow

second green third blue

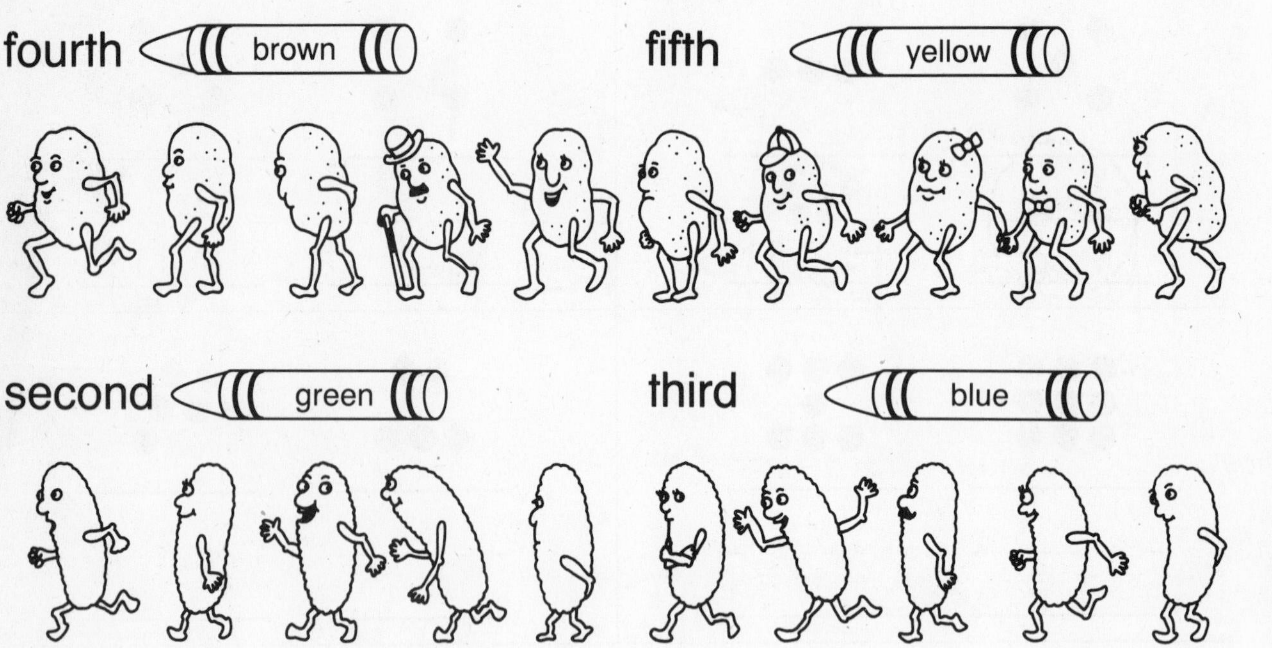

Draw 5 circles in a row.
Start at the left.
Color.

first	second	third	fourth	fifth
	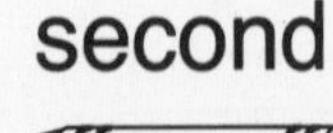	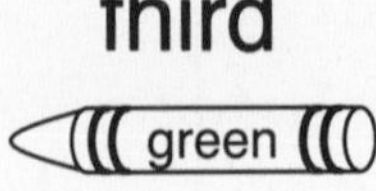		

Macmillan/McGraw-Hill, MATHEMATICS IN ACTION
Grade 1, Chapter 1, Lesson 14, pages 33–34

Name

Problem Solving Strategy: Using a Physical Model

Who has more flags?

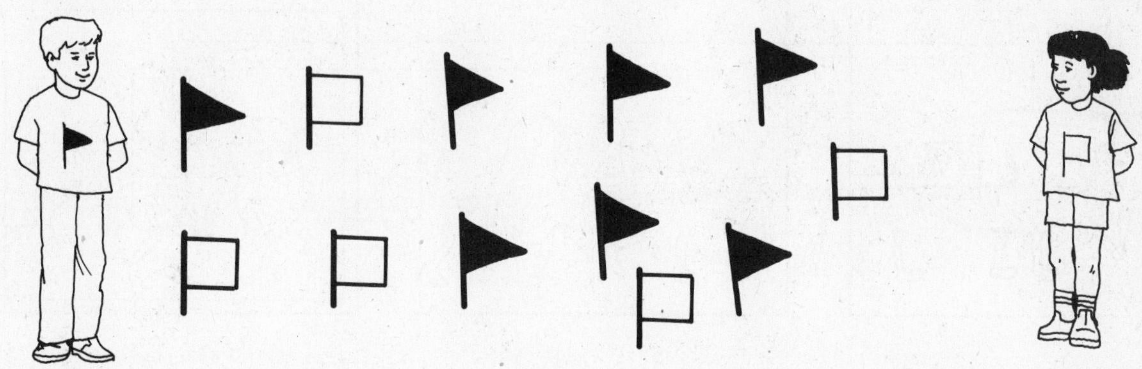

Put a yellow counter on each .

Put a red counter on each .

Make a row of yellow counters.
Make a row of red counters.
Who has more? Ring.

Which group has two more? Ring. 

Which group has two less? Ring. 

Macmillan/McGraw-Hill, MATHEMATICS IN ACTION
Grade 1, Chapter 1, Lesson 15, pages 35–36

Name

ADDITION READINESS

Use 5 ☐.

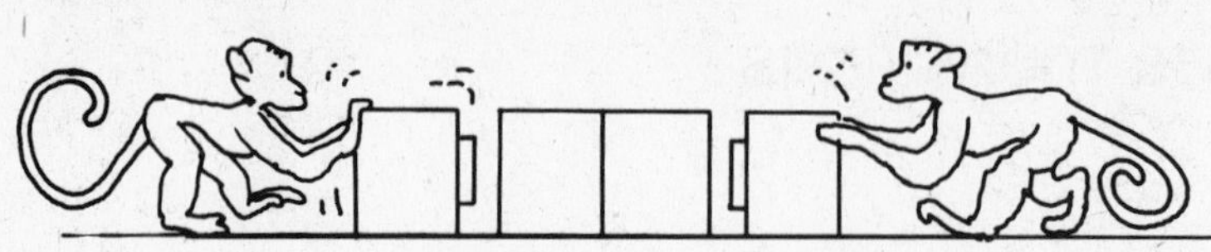

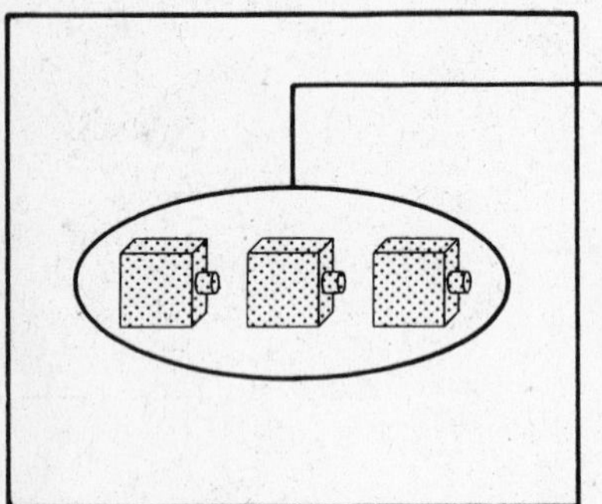

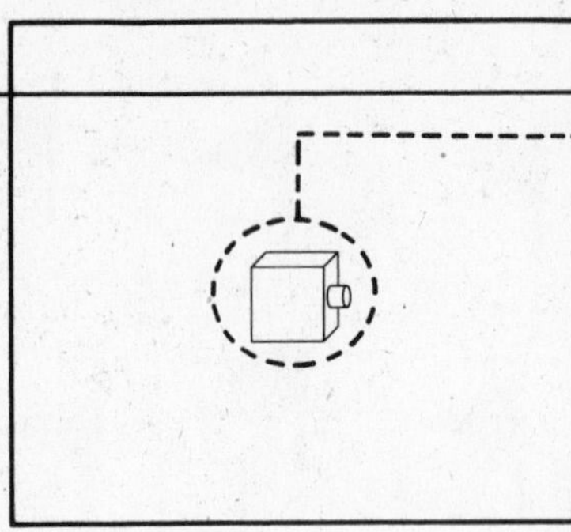

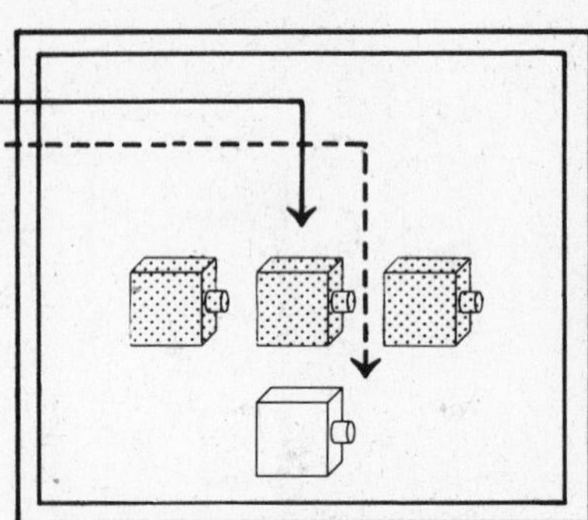

1. Put in 3. Put in 1. How many in all? 4

2. Put in 2. Put in 1. How many in all? ______

3. Put in 2. Put in 2. How many in all? ______

4. Put in 1. Put in 1. How many in all? ______

5. Put in 4. Put in 1. How many in all? ______

6. Put in 2. Put in 3. How many in all? ______

7. Put in 3. Put in 2. How many in all? ______

8. Put in 1. Put in 3. How many in all? ______

9. Put in 1. Put in 4. How many in all? ______

Name

BEGINNING ADDITION

Show with counters.
Write how many in all.

1. 1  2

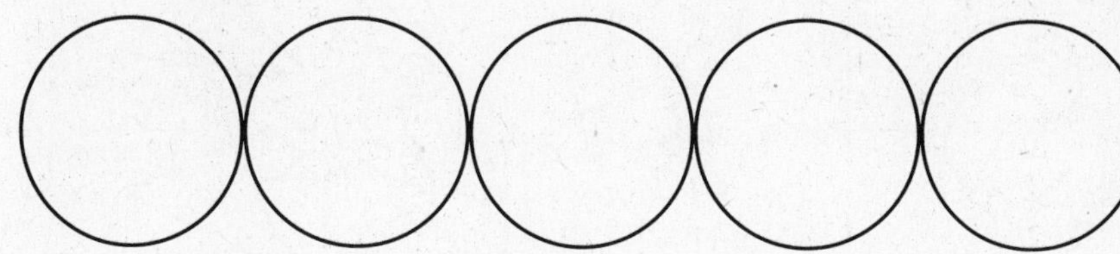

1 + 2 = 3

2. 3 2

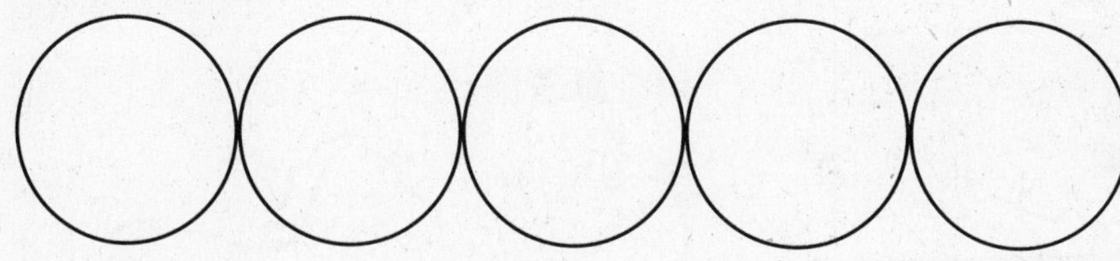

3 + 2 = ____

3. 4 1

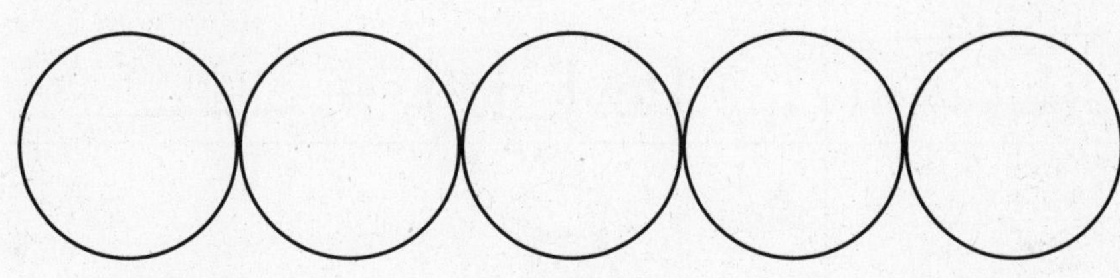

4 + 1 = ____

4. 1 3

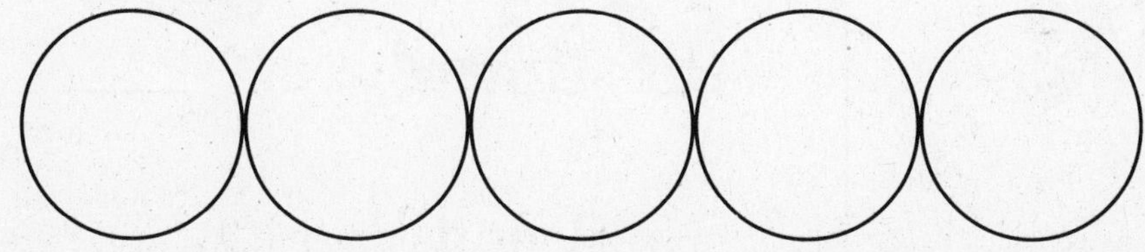

1 + 3 = ____

Name

ADDITION SENTENCES

Write how many in all.

1.

3 + 2 = 5

2.

1 + 4 = ____

3.

2 + 1 = ____

4.

1 + 1 = ____

5.

2 + 3 = ____

6.

3 + 1 = ____

Name

MORE ADDITION SENTENCES

Draw dots. Then add.

1. 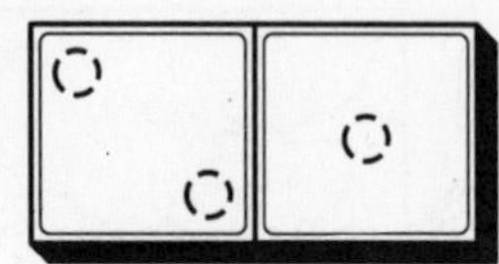

2 + 1 = 3

2. 

1 + 2 = ____

3. 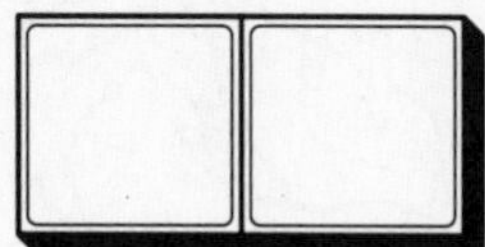

1 + 3 = ____

4. 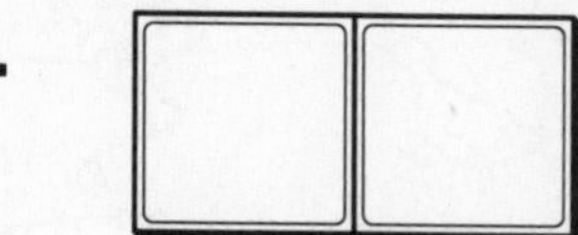

3 + 1 = ____

5. 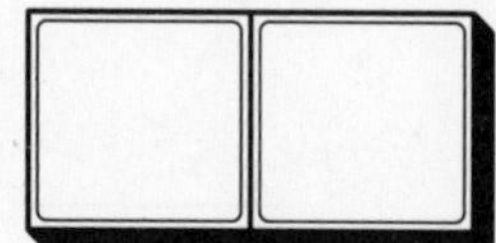

2 + 3 = ____

6. 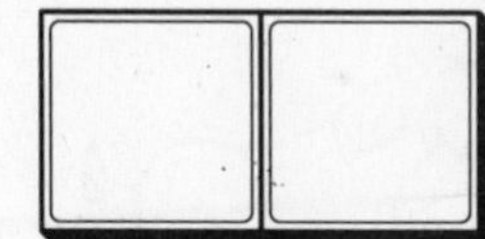

3 + 2 = ____

7. 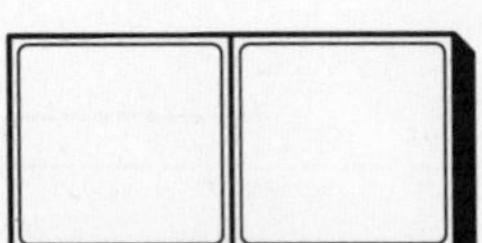

0 + 3 = ____

8. 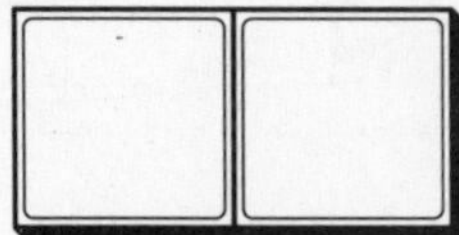

3 + 0 = ____

9. 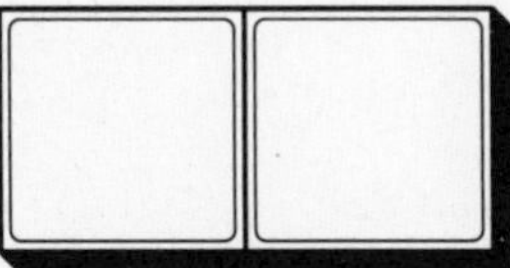

1 + 4 = ____

10. 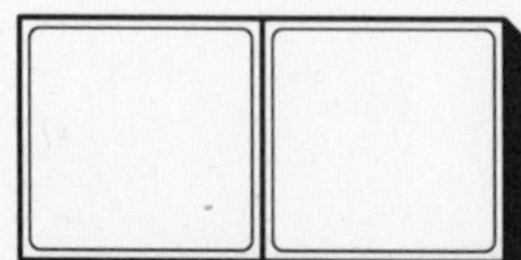

4 + 1 = ____

Macmillan/McGraw-Hill, MATHEMATICS IN ACTION
Grade 1, Chapter 2, Lesson 6, pages 55–56

Name

PROBLEM SOLVING: USING INFORMATION FROM A PICTURE

Write how many.

1. ______  ______ 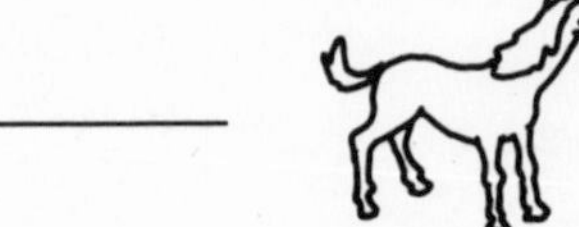 ______ in all

2. ______  ______  ______ in all

3. ______  ______  ______ in all

4. ______  ______  ______ in all

Name

COUNTING ON TO ADD

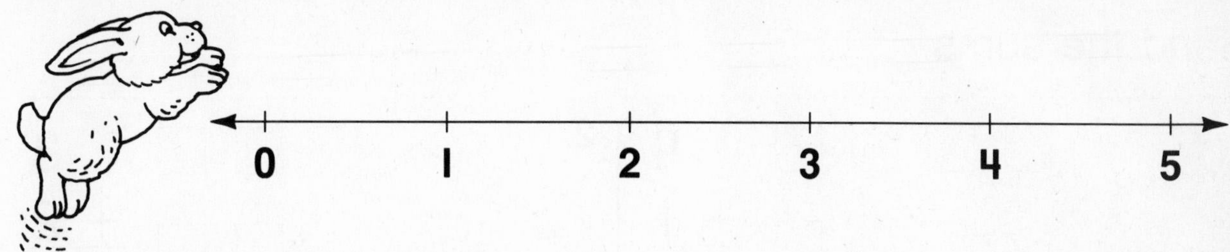

Use the number line.
Count on to add.

1. 3 + 2 = 5

2. 1 + 1 = ____

3. 4 + 1 = ____

4. 3 + 1 = ____

5. 0 + 1 = ____

6. 0 + 2 = ____

7. 2 + 1 = ____

8. 1 + 2 = ____

9. 2 + 2 = ____

10. 5 + 0 = ____

11. Start at 4.
Count on 1.
What number do you stop at? ____

12. Start at 2.
Count on 2.
What number do you stop at? ____

Macmillan/McGraw-Hill, MATHEMATICS IN ACTION
Grade 1, Chapter 2, Lesson 9, pages 61–62

Name

VERTICAL ADDITION

Find the sums.

1. 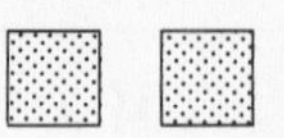

$$\begin{array}{r} 4 \\ +\ 1 \\ \hline 5 \end{array}$$

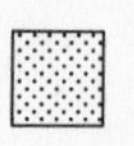

2. $$\begin{array}{r} 3 \\ +\ 2 \\ \hline \end{array}$$

3. $$\begin{array}{r} 1 \\ +\ 3 \\ \hline \end{array}$$

4. $$\begin{array}{r} 2 \\ +\ 0 \\ \hline \end{array}$$

Add. Then color.

5 red 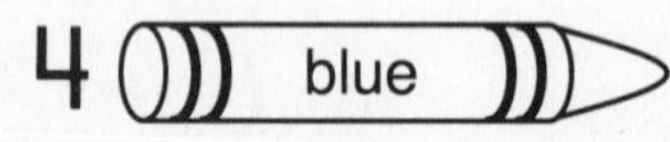 4 blue  3 or 2 yellow

3 + 2	2 + 2	1 + 2	4 + 1	0 + 4	1 + 1	5 + 0
4 + 0	0 + 2	2 + 3	1 + 3	2 + 1	1 + 4	3 + 1
3 + 0	0 + 5	2 + 2	0 + 3	3 + 2	4 + 0	2 + 0

Name

PROBLEM SOLVING STRATEGY: COMPLETING AN ADDITION SENTENCE

Complete each addition sentence.
How many in all?

1.

1 + 3 = 4

4 in all

2.

2 + 2 = ____

____ in all

3.

2 + 3 = ____

____ in all

4.

4 + 1 = ____

____ in all

Macmillan/McGraw-Hill, MATHEMATICS IN ACTION
Grade 1, Chapter 2, Lesson 11, pages 65–66

Name

SUBTRACTION READINESS

Use 5 [cube].

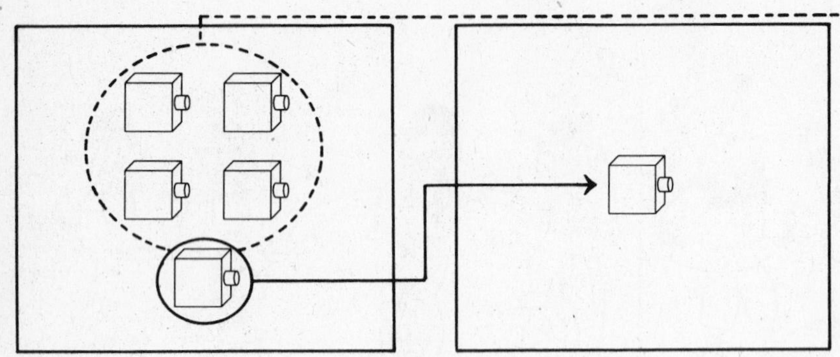

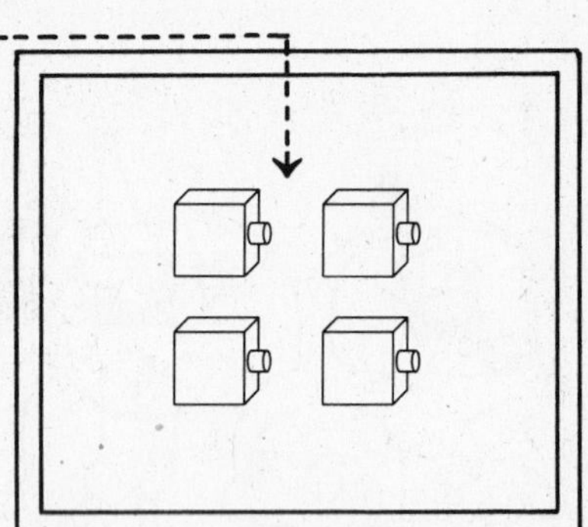

1. Put in 5. Take away 1. How many are left? 4
2. Put in 2. Take away 1. How many are left? ______
3. Put in 3. Take away 2. How many are left? ______
4. Put in 4. Take away 2. How many are left? ______
5. Put in 5. Take away 3. How many are left? ______
6. Put in 4. Take away 3. How many are left? ______
7. Put in 5. Take away 2. How many are left? ______
8. Put in 4. Take away 1. How many are left? ______
9. Put in 3. Take away 1. How many are left? ______

Name

BEGINNING SUBTRACTION

Show with counters.
Write how many are left.

1. Show 5 ◯. Take away 3 ◯.

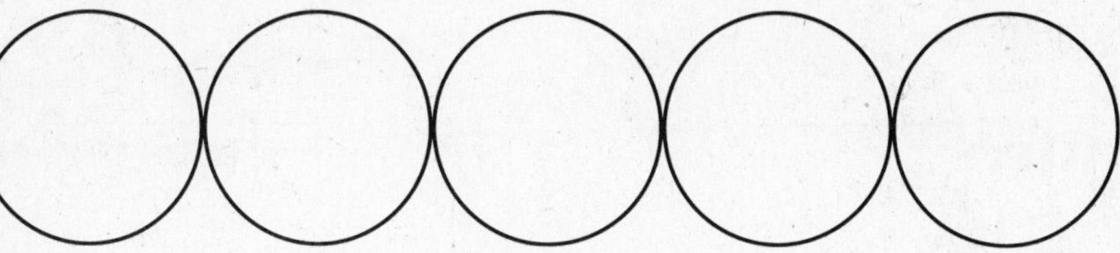

5 − 3 = 2

2. Show 3 ◯. Take away 2 ◯.

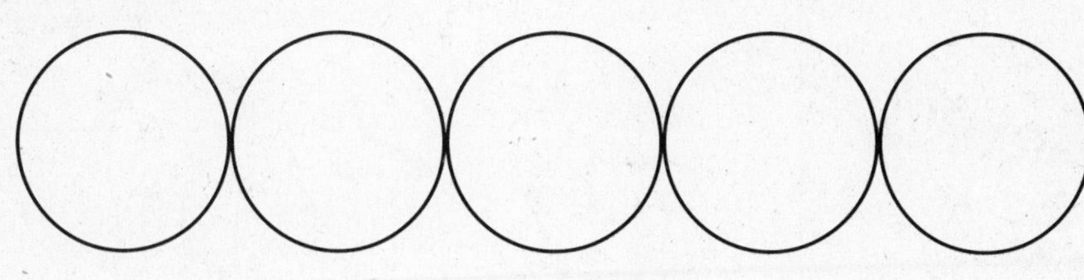

3 − 2 = ____

3. Show 4 ◯. Take away 1 ◯.

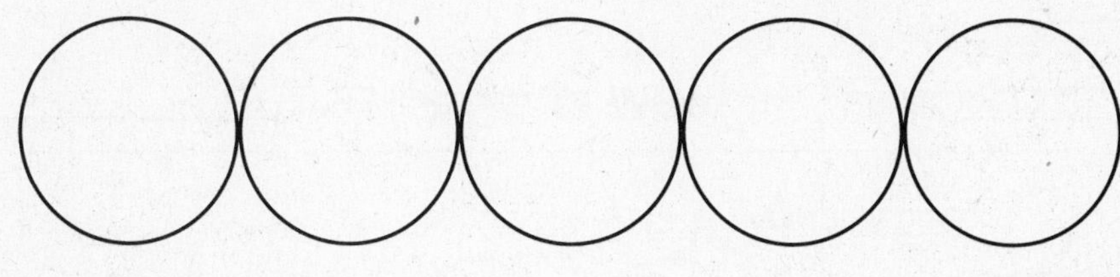

4 − 1 = ____

4. Show 5 ◯. Take away 4 ◯.

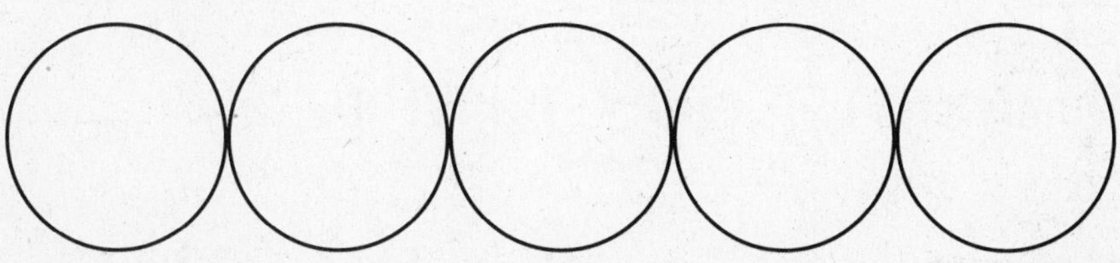

5 − 4 = ____

Name

SUBTRACTION SENTENCES

Write how many are left.

1.

4 − 3 = 1

2.

3 − 1 = ____

3.

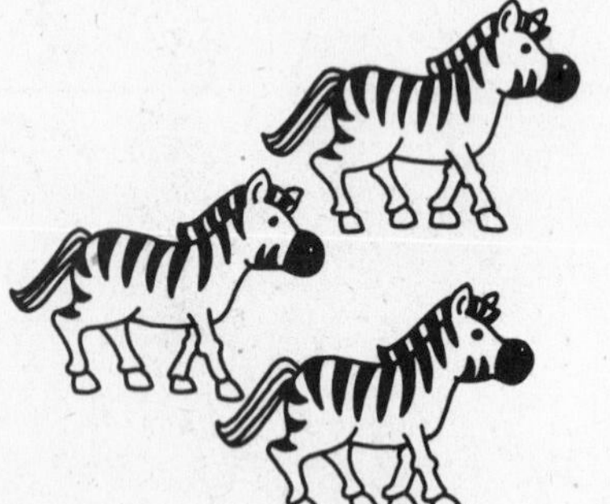

5 − 3 = ____

4.

3 − 2 = ____

5.

4 − 2 = ____

6.

5 − 1 = ____

Name

MORE SUBTRACTION SENTENCES

Cross out to help you subtract.

1. 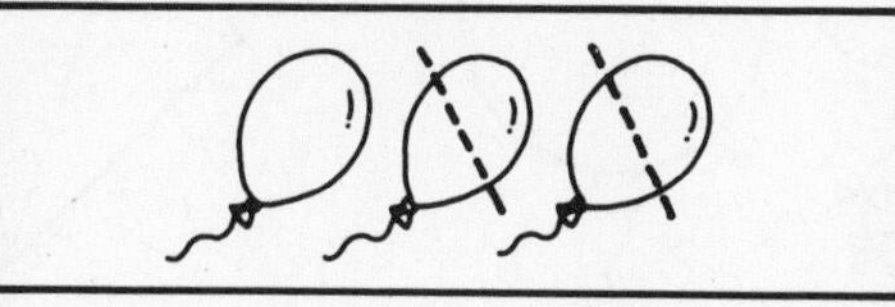

$3 - 2 =$ 1

2. 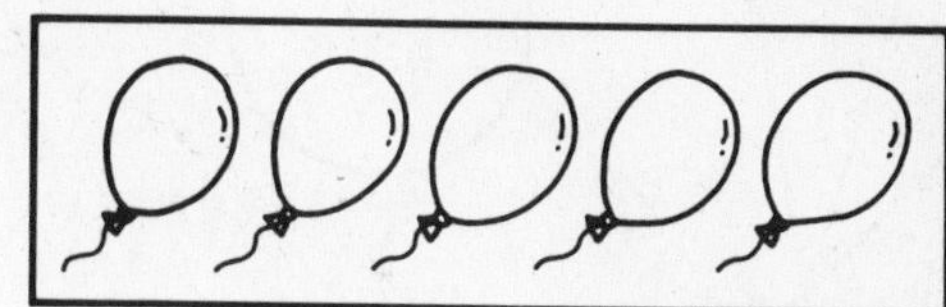

$5 - 1 =$ ____

3. 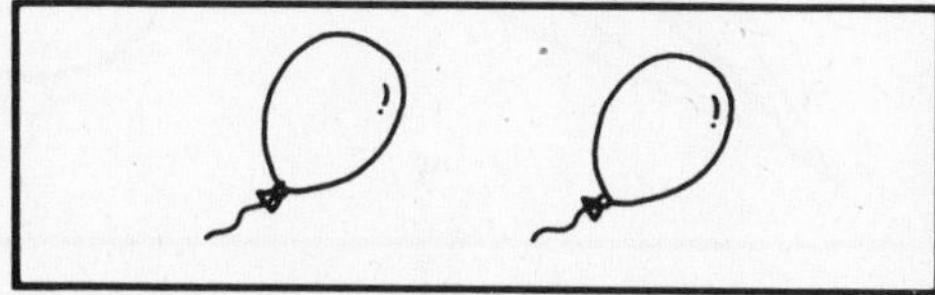

$2 - 2 =$ ____

4. 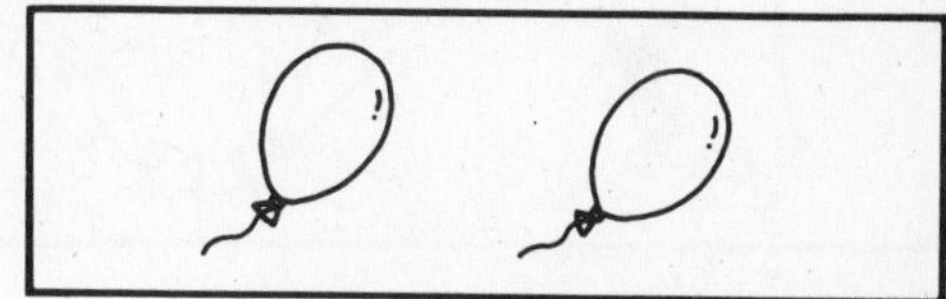

$2 - 1 =$ ____

5. 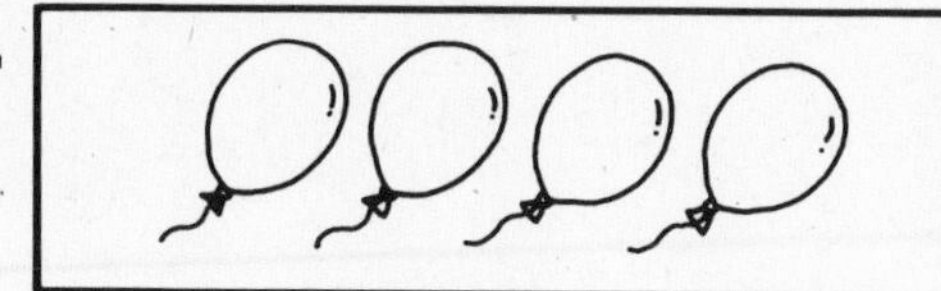

$4 - 4 =$ ____

6. 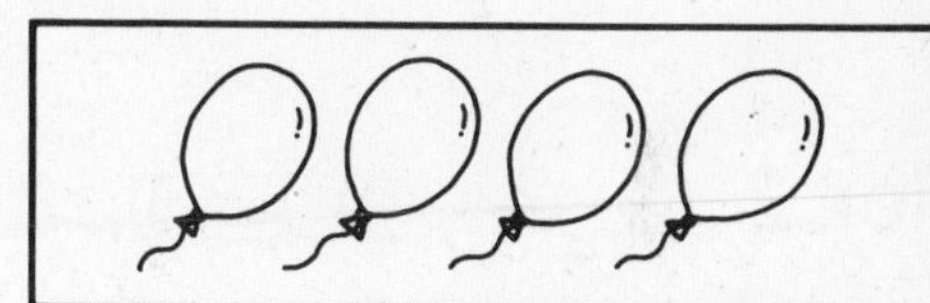

$4 - 0 =$ ____

7. 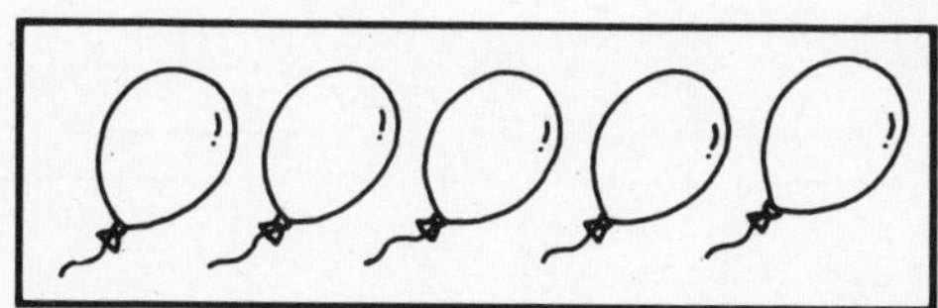

$5 - 2 =$ ____

8. 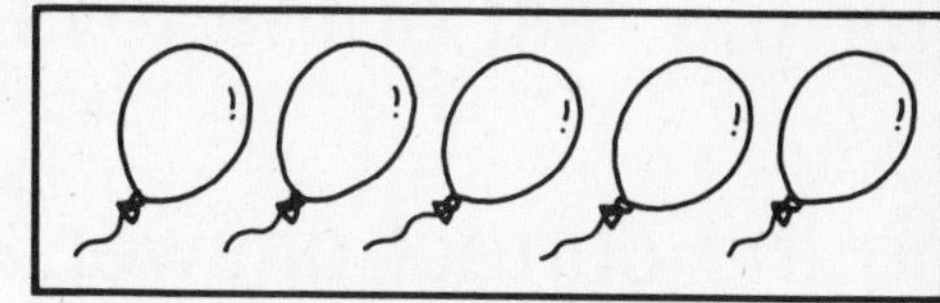

$5 - 3 =$ ____

9. 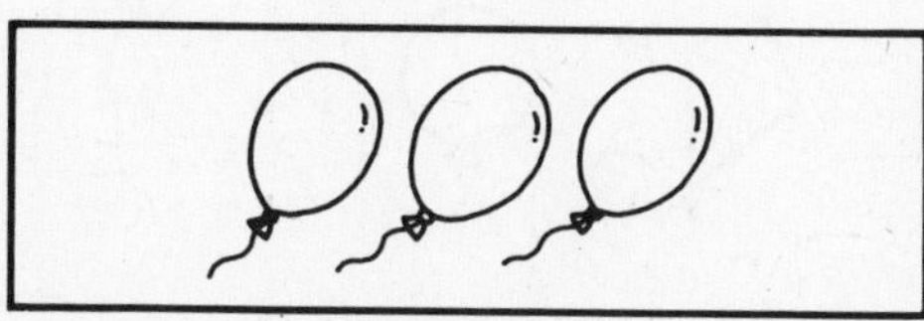

$3 - 1 =$ ____

10. 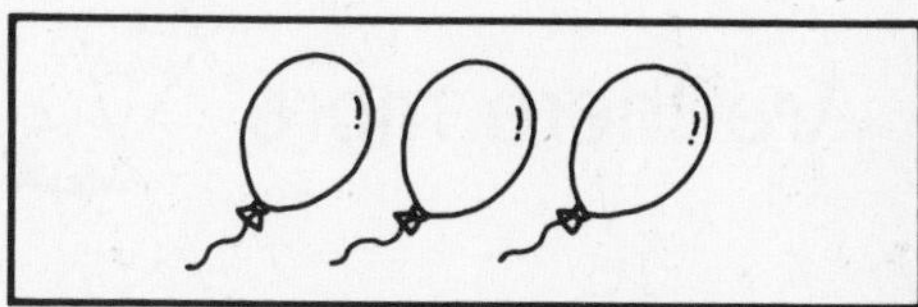

$3 - 2 =$ ____

Macmillan/McGraw-Hill, MATHEMATICS IN ACTION
Grade 1, Chapter 3, Lesson 6, pages 85–86

Name

Problem Solving Strategy: Using Number Sense

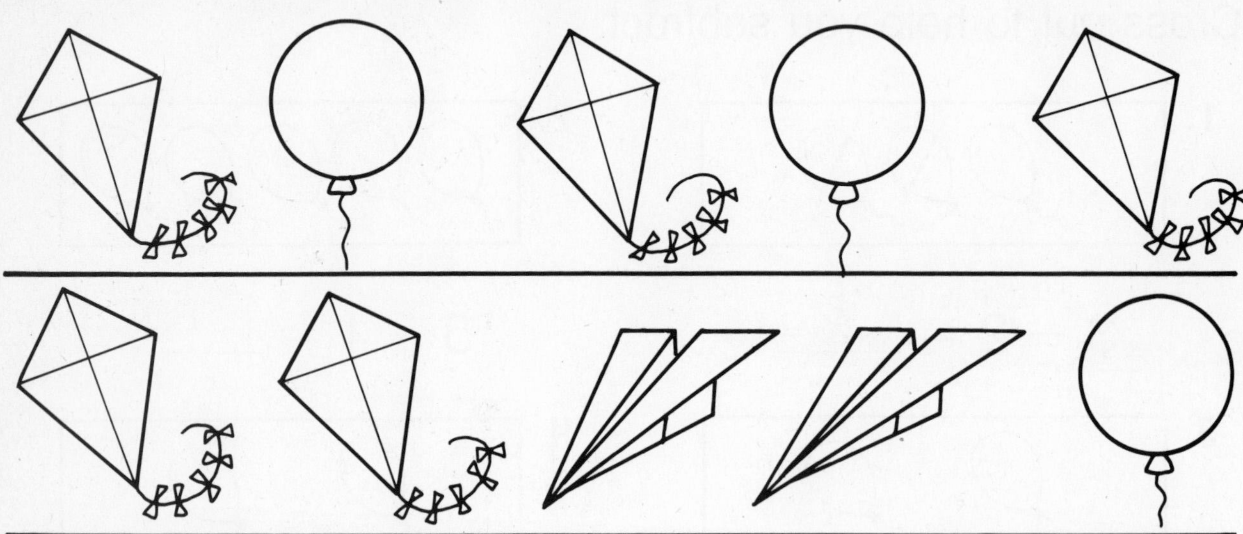

Color 2 kites red.

Color 2 balloons red.

Color 2 planes red.

Color the rest of the toys yellow.

Ring the correct answer.

1. Are there more red toys or yellow toys?

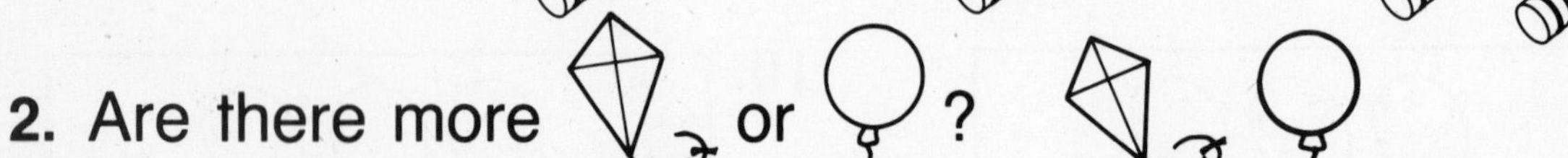

2. Are there more kites or balloons?

3. Are there more kites, balloons, or planes?

MACMILLAN/McGRAW-HILL

Name

Counting back to subtract

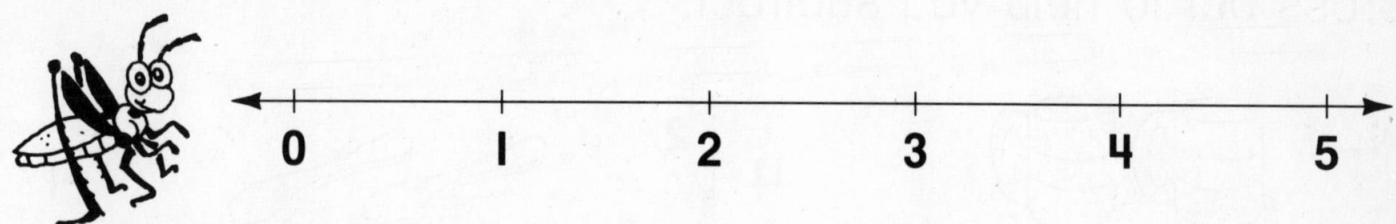

Use the number line.
Count back to subtract.

1. 5 − 1 = 4

2. 3 − 3 = ____

3. 4 − 2 = ____

4. 5 − 2 = ____

5. 2 − 1 = ____

6. 3 − 2 = ____

7. 1 − 1 = ____

8. 4 − 1 = ____

9. 2 − 2 = ____

10. 3 − 1 = ____

11. Start at 4.
Count back 2.
What number do you stop at? ____

12. Start at 3.
Count back 1.
What number do you stop at? ____

Macmillan/McGraw-Hill, MATHEMATICS IN ACTION
Grade 1, Chapter 3, Lesson 9, pages 91–92

Name

VERTICAL SUBTRACTION

Cross out to help you subtract.

1. 

$$\begin{array}{r} 4 \\ -\ 1 \\ \hline 3 \end{array}$$

2. 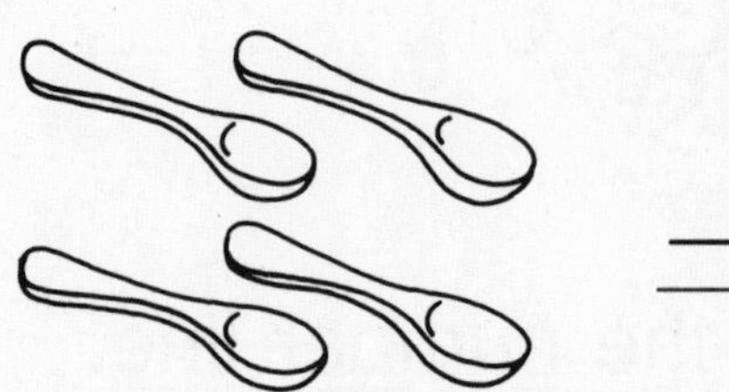

$$\begin{array}{r} 4 \\ -\ 3 \\ \hline \end{array}$$

3. 

$$\begin{array}{r} 5 \\ -\ 3 \\ \hline \end{array}$$

4. 

$$\begin{array}{r} 5 \\ -\ 2 \\ \hline \end{array}$$

Subtract.

5. $\begin{array}{r} 3 \\ -\ 2 \\ \hline \end{array}$ $\begin{array}{r} 3 \\ -\ 1 \\ \hline \end{array}$ $\begin{array}{r} 5 \\ -\ 1 \\ \hline \end{array}$ $\begin{array}{r} 5 \\ -\ 4 \\ \hline \end{array}$ $\begin{array}{r} 2 \\ -\ 0 \\ \hline \end{array}$ $\begin{array}{r} 2 \\ -\ 2 \\ \hline \end{array}$

6. $\begin{array}{r} 4 \\ -\ 2 \\ \hline \end{array}$ $\begin{array}{r} 2 \\ -\ 1 \\ \hline \end{array}$ $\begin{array}{r} 3 \\ -\ 3 \\ \hline \end{array}$ $\begin{array}{r} 4 \\ -\ 0 \\ \hline \end{array}$ $\begin{array}{r} 2 \\ -\ 1 \\ \hline \end{array}$ $\begin{array}{r} 5 \\ -\ 0 \\ \hline \end{array}$

7. $\begin{array}{r} 1 \\ -\ 0 \\ \hline \end{array}$ $\begin{array}{r} 5 \\ -\ 2 \\ \hline \end{array}$ $\begin{array}{r} 4 \\ -\ 3 \\ \hline \end{array}$ $\begin{array}{r} 1 \\ -\ 1 \\ \hline \end{array}$ $\begin{array}{r} 3 \\ -\ 0 \\ \hline \end{array}$ $\begin{array}{r} 4 \\ -\ 4 \\ \hline \end{array}$

Name

FACT FAMILIES

Complete each fact family.
Add or subtract.

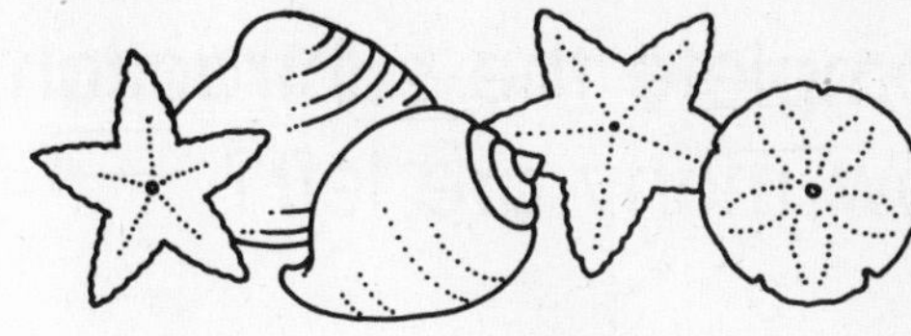

1. 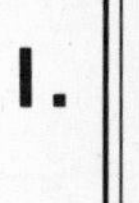 

3	2	5	5
+ 2	+ 3	− 2	− 3
5		3	

2. 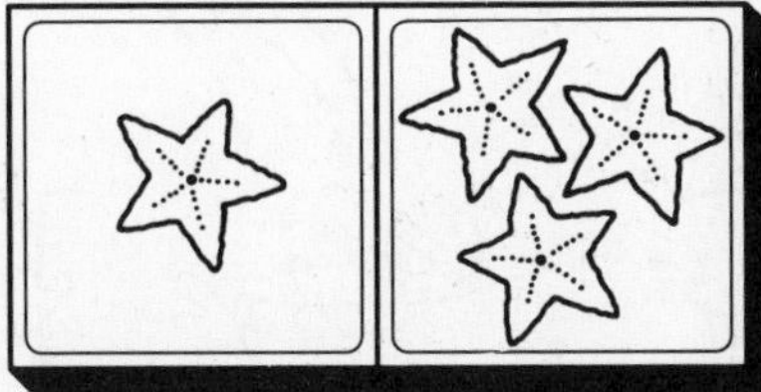

1	3	4	4
+ 3	+ 1	− 1	− 3

3. 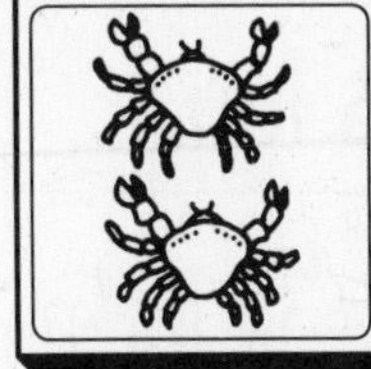 

2	1	3	3
+ 1	+ 2	− 2	− 1

4. 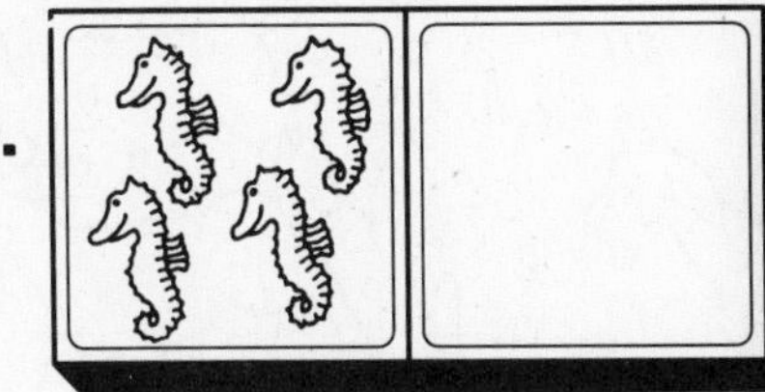

4	0	4	4
+ 0	+ 4	− 0	− 4

5. 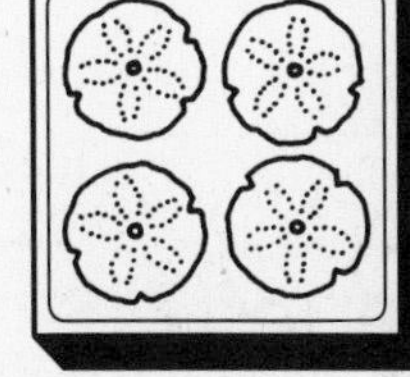

2	4
+ 2	− 2

6. 

1	2
+ 1	− 1

Macmillan/McGraw-Hill, MATHEMATICS IN ACTION
Grade 1, Chapter 3, Lesson 11, pages 95–96

Name

PROBLEM SOLVING STRATEGY: COMPLETING A SUBTRACTION SENTENCE

Complete the subtraction sentence.
How many are left?

1.

5 − 1 = 4

4 are left

2.

5 − 3 = ____

____ are left

3.

4 − 1 = ____

____ are left

4.

5 − 2 = ____

____ are left

Name

COUNTING ON

Count on to add.

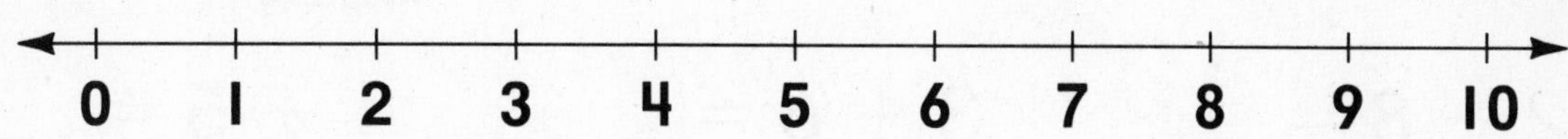

1. 5 + 2 = 7　　7 + 2 = ____　　7 + 1 = ____

2. 8 + 2 = ____　　4 + 1 = ____　　3 + 3 = ____

3. 9 + 1 = ____　　5 + 3 = ____　　4 + 2 = ____

4. 4 + 3 = ____　　6 + 2 = ____　　5 + 1 = ____

5. 2 + 2 = ____　　8 + 1 = ____　　6 + 3 = ____

6. 6 + 1 = ____　　7 + 3 = ____　　3 + 2 = ____

7. 2 + 1 = ____　　3 + 1 = ____　　1 + 2 = ____

8. Kim had 6 fish.

She got 2 more fish.

How many fish does she have in all? ____ 

Macmillan/McGraw-Hill, MATHEMATICS IN ACTION
Grade 1, Chapter 4, Lesson 3, pages 113–114

Name

USING THE LARGER NUMBER FIRST

Count on to add.
Begin with the larger number.

1. 2 + 8 = 10 3 + 6 = ____ 1 + 5 = ____
2. 1 + 9 = ____ 7 + 2 = ____ 2 + 6 = ____
3. 6 + 2 = ____ 2 + 7 = ____ 8 + 1 = ____
4. 1 + 3 = ____ 1 + 8 = ____ 3 + 7 = ____
5. 3 + 5 = ____ 7 + 1 = ____ 1 + 6 = ____
6. 1 + 7 = ____ 8 + 2 = ____ 9 + 1 = ____
7. 6 + 1 = ____ 1 + 4 = ____ 2 + 5 = ____

Draw a line to the sum.

8. 1 + 9	10	7 + 2
	9	
9. 6 + 1		9 + 1
	8	
10. 2 + 7	7	1 + 6

Name

PATTERNS

Add. Look for patterns.
Ring the sums if there is a pattern.

1.	8	7	6	5	4	3
	+ 2	+ 2	+ 2	+ 2	+ 2	+ 2
	10					
2.	1	2	1	1	2	3
	+ 1	+ 3	+ 4	+ 7	+ 6	+ 4
3.	5	5	5	5	5	5
	+ 5	+ 4	+ 3	+ 2	+ 1	+ 0
4.	2	3	4	5	6	7
	+ 0	+ 0	+ 0	+ 0	+ 0	+ 0
5.	4	4	4	4	4	4
	+ 1	+ 2	+ 3	+ 4	+ 5	+ 6

Name

Using doubles

Add.

Count on. Use doubles. Use ◯.

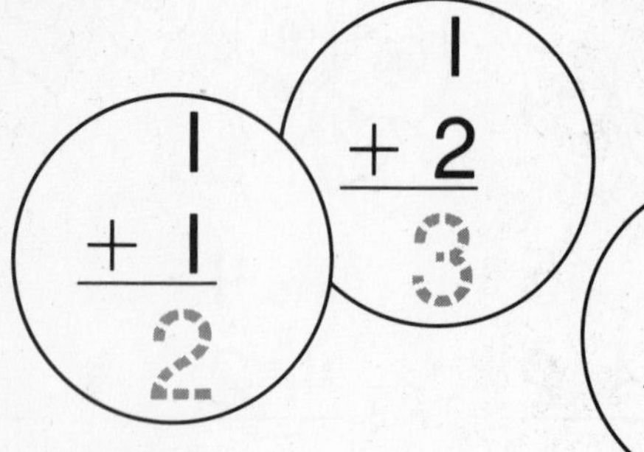

$2 + 3$

$2 + 2$

$3 + 3$

$3 + 4$

$3 + 2$

$4 + 4$

$4 + 5$

$2 + 1$

$8 + 0$

$4 + 3$

$5 + 5$

$5 + 4$

$7 + 3$

$1 + 8$

$7 + 2$

$9 + 1$

$1 + 7$

$8 + 2$

$2 + 7$

$3 + 6$

$0 + 9$

$6 + 4$

Macmillan/McGraw-Hill, MATHEMATICS IN ACTION
Grade 1, Chapter 4, Lesson 6, pages 117–118

MACMILLAN/McGRAW-HILL

Name

PROBLEM SOLVING STRATEGY: WRITING AN ADDITION SENTENCE

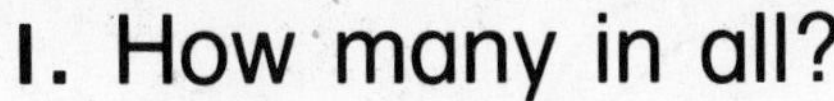

1. How many in all?

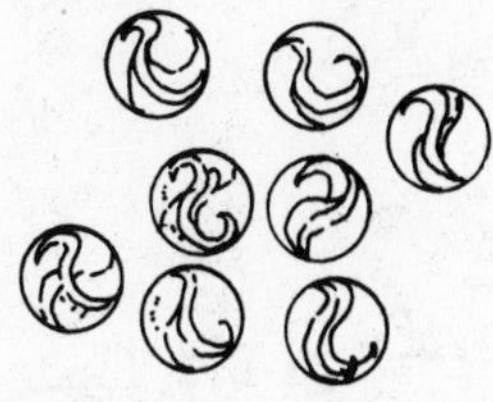

_____ + _____ = _____

_____ in all

2. How many [jack] are there?

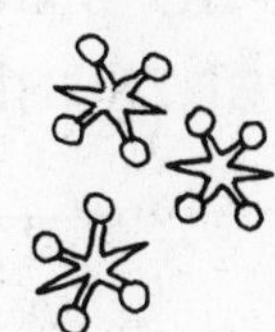
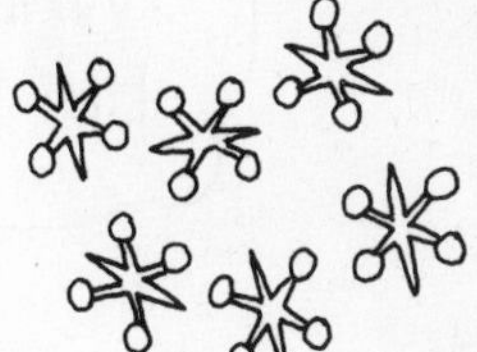

_____ + _____ = _____

_____ [jack]

3. How many altogether?

_____ + _____ = _____

_____ altogether

4. How many in all?

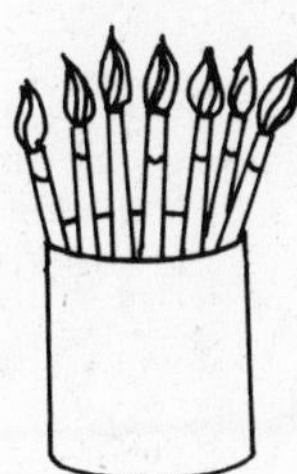
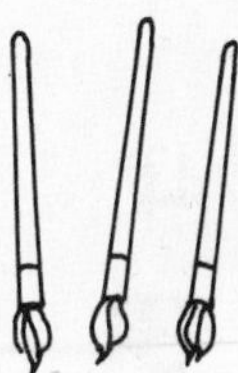

_____ + _____ = _____

_____ in all

5. How many  in all?

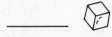

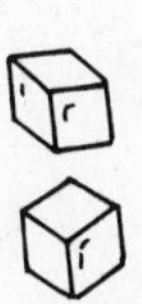
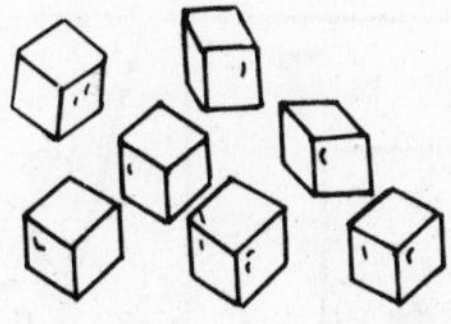

_____ + _____ = _____

_____ [cube]

6. How many altogether?

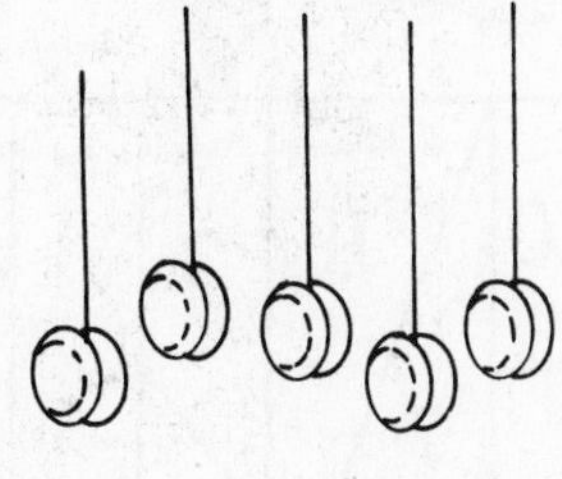
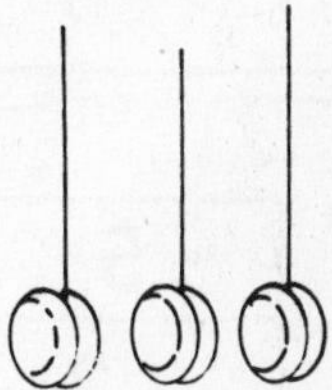

_____ + _____ = _____

_____ altogether

Name

ADDING THREE NUMBERS

What can be plowed but is never planted?

Add.

1.

1	6	5
2	1	4
+ 3	+ 1	+ 1

4	6	1
3	3	1
+ 0	+ 1	+ 1

2.

2	1	4
5	1	0
+ 2	+ 3	+ 1

1	6	2
0	2	1
+ 1	+ 1	+ 1

Color these answers yellow.

Color these answers blue.

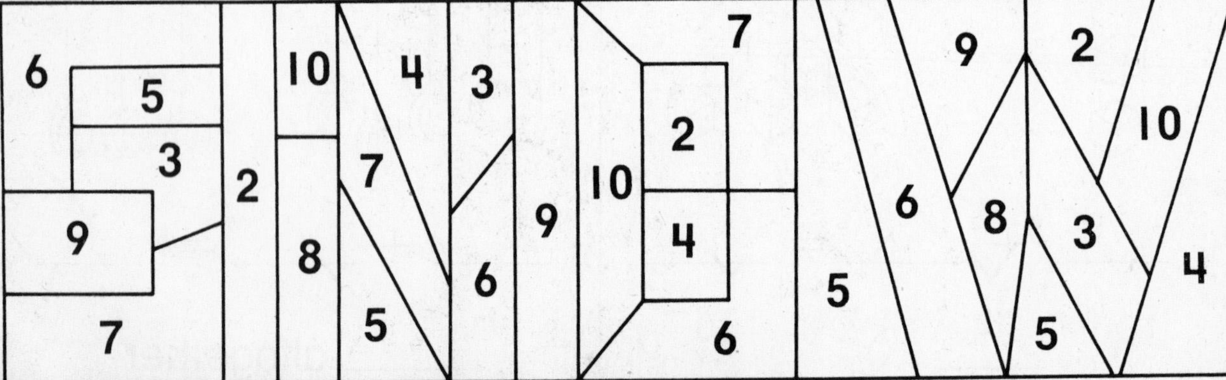

Name

PROBLEM SOLVING STRATEGY: LOOKING FOR A PATTERN

Color and continue the pattern.

1.

red blue red blue red blue

2.

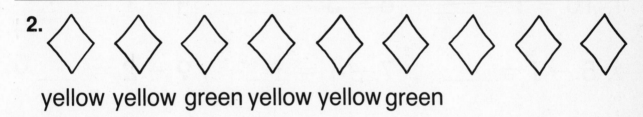

yellow yellow green yellow yellow green

3.
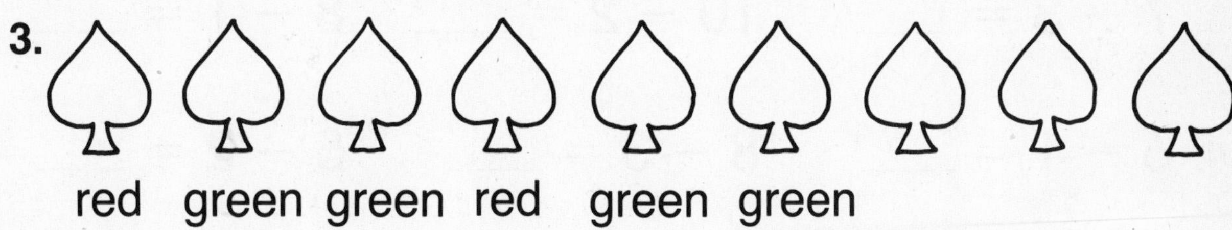

red green green red green green

4.
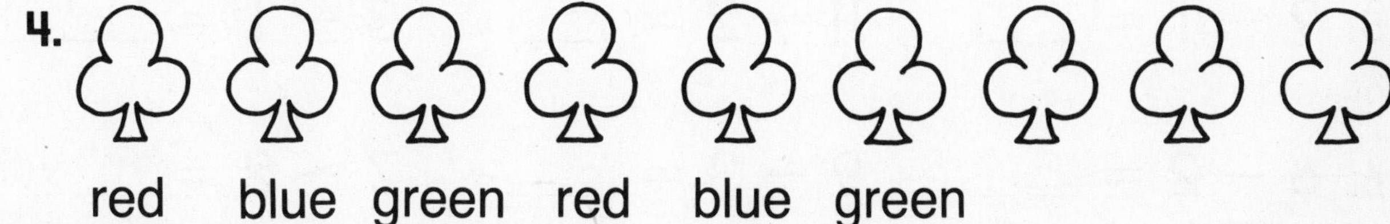

red blue green red blue green

5.

red red yellow yellow red red yellow yellow

6.
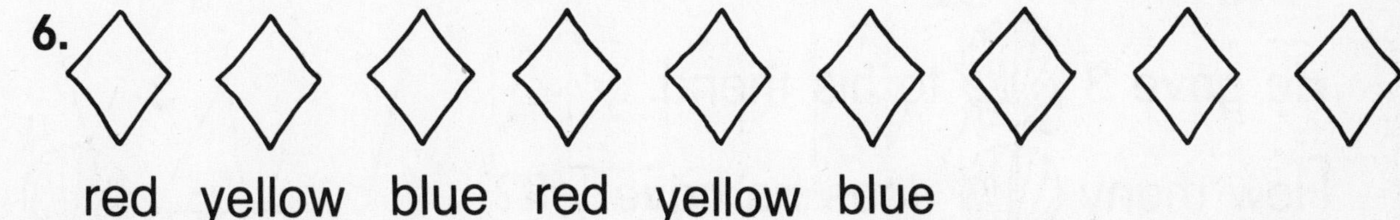

red yellow blue red yellow blue

Macmillan/McGraw-Hill, MATHEMATICS IN ACTION
Grade 1, Chapter 4, Lesson 10, pages 125–126

Name

COUNTING BACK TO SUBTRACT

Count back.

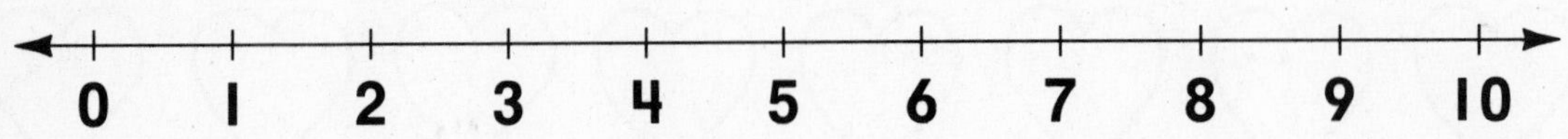

1. 10 − 1 = 9　　6 − 3 = ___　　4 − 1 = ___

2. 5 − 1 = ___　　7 − 1 = ___　　9 − 2 = ___

3. 7 − 3 = ___　　10 − 2 = ___　　8 − 1 = ___

4. 6 − 1 = ___　　8 − 3 = ___　　5 − 2 = ___

5. 9 − 1 = ___　　4 − 2 = ___　　3 − 1 = ___

6. 6 − 2 = ___　　9 − 3 = ___　　7 − 2 = ___

7. 8 − 2 = ___　　5 − 3 = ___　　10 − 3 = ___

8. Greg found 8 .

He gave 3  to his friend.

How many does he have left? 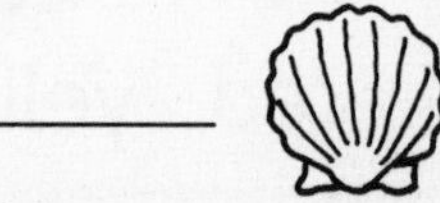

Name

USING RELATED SUBTRACTION FACTS

Complete each pair of facts.

1.
5 − 4 = 1
5 − 1 = 4

2.
8 − 3 = ____
8 − 5 = ____

4.
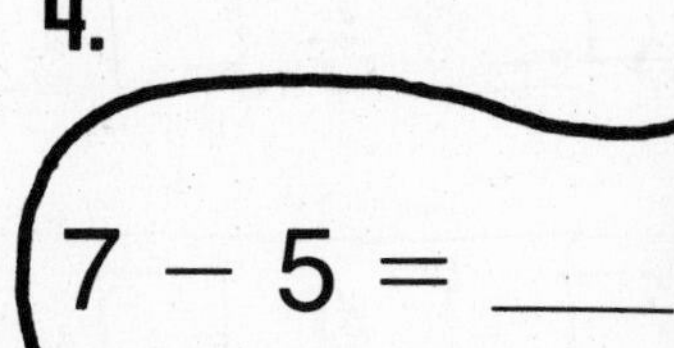
7 − 5 = ____
7 − 2 = ____

3.
8 − 6 = ____
8 − 2 = ____

5.
10 − 4 = ____
10 − 6 = ____

7.
9 − 2 = ____
9 − 7 = ____

6.
10 − 3 = ____
10 − 7 = ____

8.
9 − 5 = ____
9 − 4 = ____

Macmillan/McGraw-Hill, MATHEMATICS IN ACTION
Grade 1, Chapter 5, Lesson 4, page 143

Name

SUBTRACTION PATTERNS

Subtract. Look for patterns.

1.

2.

3.

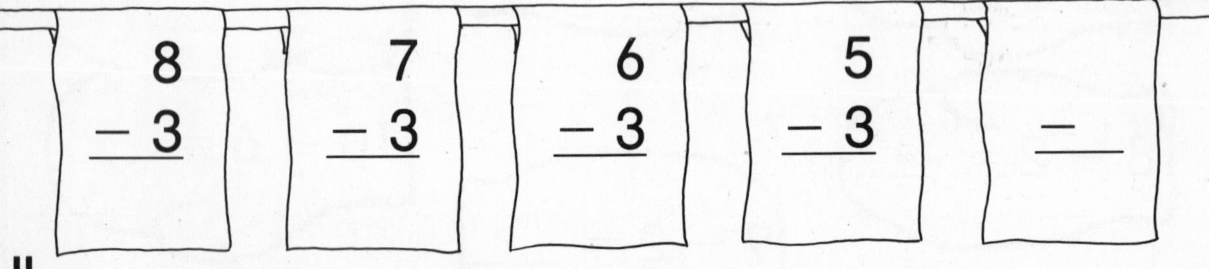

4.

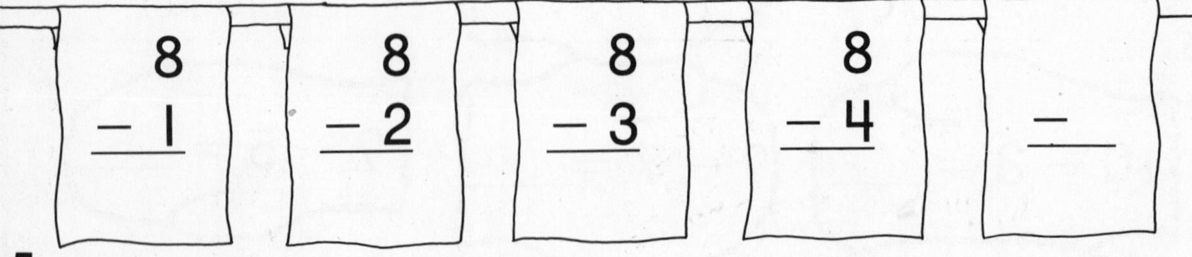

5.

Name

PROBLEM SOLVING STRATEGY: WRITING A SUBTRACTION SENTENCE

How many are left?

1.

7 – 3 = 4

4 are left

2.

_____ – _____ = _____

_____ are left

3.

_____ – _____ = _____

_____ are left

4.

_____ – _____ = _____

_____ are left

5.

_____ – _____ = _____

_____ are left

6.

_____ – _____ = _____

_____ are left

Macmillan/McGraw-Hill, MATHEMATICS IN ACTION
Grade 1, Chapter 5, Lesson 6, pages 145–146

Name ___

SUBTRACTION AND ADDITION

Write the missing numbers.
Use ◯ if you need help.

1. 8 − 2 = 6   10 − 5 = ___   9 − 3 = ___

   2 + 6 = 8   5 + ___ = 10   3 + ___ = 9

2. 9 − 5 = ___   7 − 4 = ___   10 − 2 = ___

   5 + ___ = 9   4 + ___ = 7   2 + ___ = 10

3. 10 − 6 = ___   8 − 5 = ___   9 − 1 = ___

   6 + ___ = 10   5 + ___ = 8   1 + ___ = 9

4. 7 − 5 = ___   9 − 2 = ___   8 − 4 = ___

   5 + ___ = 7   2 + ___ = 9   4 + ___ = 8

Name

FACT FAMILIES

Complete each fact family.

1. $8 + 2 =$ 10 $10 - 2 =$ 8

$2 + 8 =$ ____ $10 - 8 =$ ____

2. $1 + 9 =$ ____ $10 - 9 =$ ____

$9 + 1 =$ ____ $10 - 1 =$ ____

3. $6 + 3 =$ ____ $9 - 3 =$ ____

$3 + 6 =$ ____ $9 - 6 =$ ____

4. 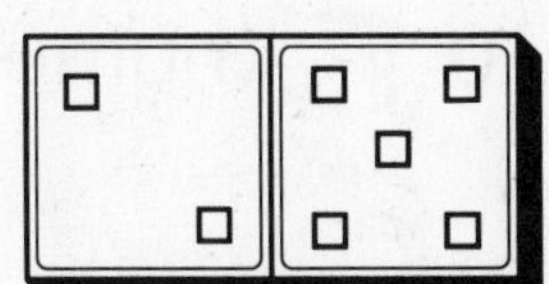

$2 + 5 =$ ____ $7 - 5 =$ ____

$5 + 2 =$ ____ $7 - 2 =$ ____

5. 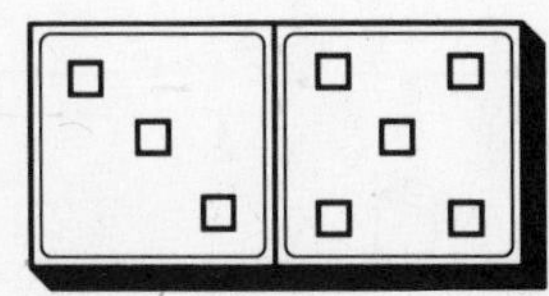

$3 + 5 =$ ____ $8 - 5 =$ ____

$5 + 3 =$ ____ $8 - 3 =$ ____

Macmillan/McGraw-Hill, MATHEMATICS IN ACTION
Grade 1, Chapter 5, Lesson 9, pages 151–152

Name

PROBLEM SOLVING STRATEGY: USING A PHYSICAL MODEL

Solve. Use counters for help.

1. James had 10  .

   He put 3  away.

   How many 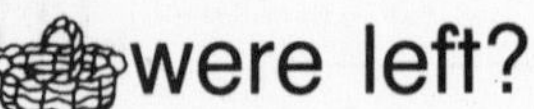 were left?

   _____ – _____ = _____

   _____ were left.

2. There were 9  .

   The store sold 4 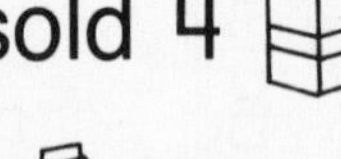 .

   How many  were left?

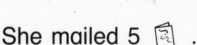

   _____ – _____ = _____

   _____ were left.

3. 7 were on the swings.

   1  got off.

   How many were left?

   _____ – _____ = _____

   _____ were left.

4. Judy wrote 8  .

   She mailed 5  .

   How many were left?

   _____ – _____ = _____

   _____

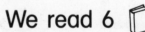

5. Jack picked 6  .

   He put 4 in a vase.

   How many were left?

   _____ – _____ = _____

   _____ were left.

6. We took 10 home.

   We read 6  .

   How many  were left?

   _____ – _____ = _____

   _____ 

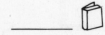

Name

PROBLEM SOLVING STRATEGY: CHOOSING THE OPERATION

Ring the number sentence that solves the problem.

1. Lee had 5 pencils.
He found 5 more pencils.
How many pencils in all?

$5 - 5 = 0$

$5 + 5 = 10$

2. Maria had 4 books.
She got 3 more books.
How many books in all?

$4 + 3 = 7$

$4 - 3 = 1$

3. Evan had 6 pencils.
He gave away 4 pencils.
How many pencils were left?

$6 + 4 = 10$

$6 - 4 = 2$

4. Leslie had 8 books.
She returned 2 books.
How many books were left?

$8 - 2 = 6$

$8 + 2 = 10$

5. Tommy had 3 pencils.
He got 2 more pencils.
How many pencils in all?

$3 - 2 = 1$

$3 + 2 = 5$

6. Mandy had 5 books.
She returned 4 books.
How many books were left?

$5 - 4 = 1$

$5 + 4 = 9$

Macmillan/McGraw-Hill, MATHEMATICS IN ACTION
Grade 1, Chapter 6, Lesson 7, pages 177–178

Name

NUMBERS TO 79

Color the correct number of tens and ones.

1. 78 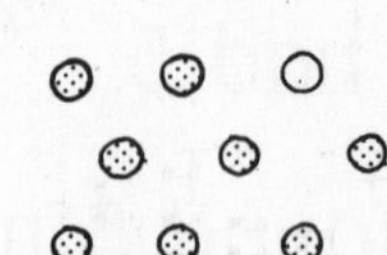

2. 65 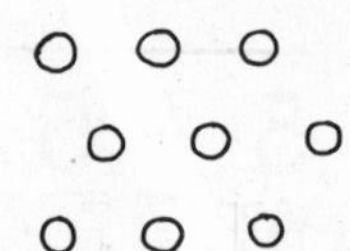

3. 73 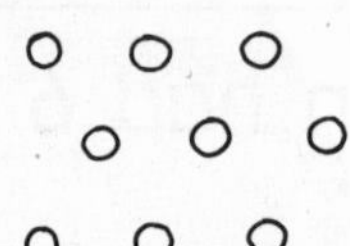

Write the numbers.

4. 

tens	ones

______

5. 

tens	ones

______

6.

tens	ones

______

7. 

tens	ones

______

PRACTICE-53

Name ______________________________

SKIP-COUNTING

Count by twos.

1. 2, 4, ____, ____, ____, ____, ____, ____

2. 36, 38, ____, ____, ____, ____, ____, ____

Count by fives.

3. 5, 10, ____, ____, ____, ____, ____, ____

4. 30, 35, ____, ____, ____, ____, ____, ____

Connect the dots in order.

5. Skip-count by twos.

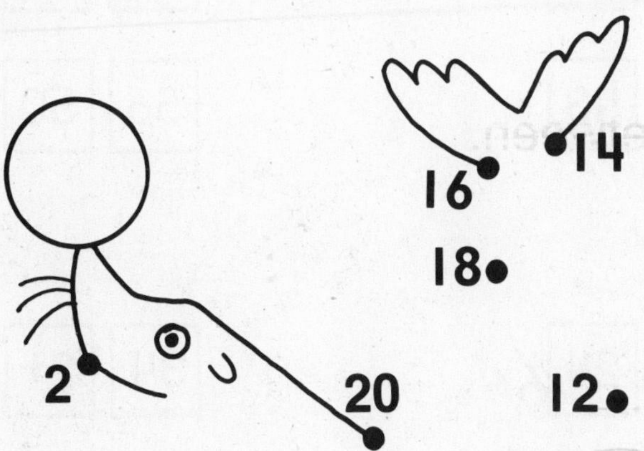

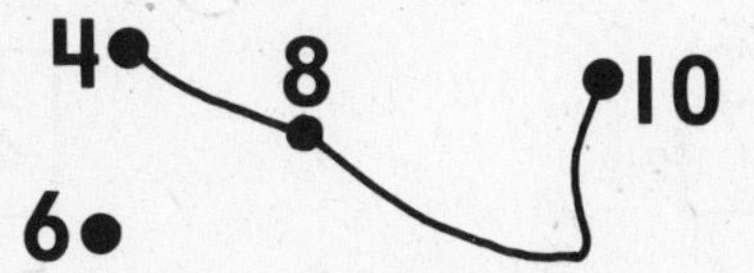

6. Skip-count by fives.

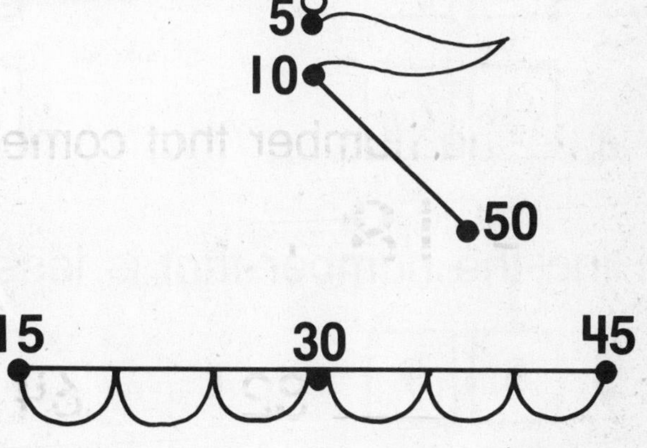

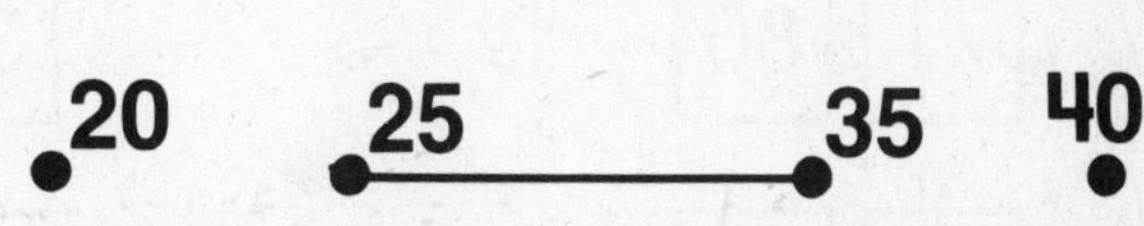

MACMILLAN/McGRAW-HILL

Macmillan/McGraw-Hill, MATHEMATICS IN ACTION
Grade 1, Chapter 6, Lesson 12, pages 187–188

Name

GREATER AND LESS

1. Ring the number that is greater.

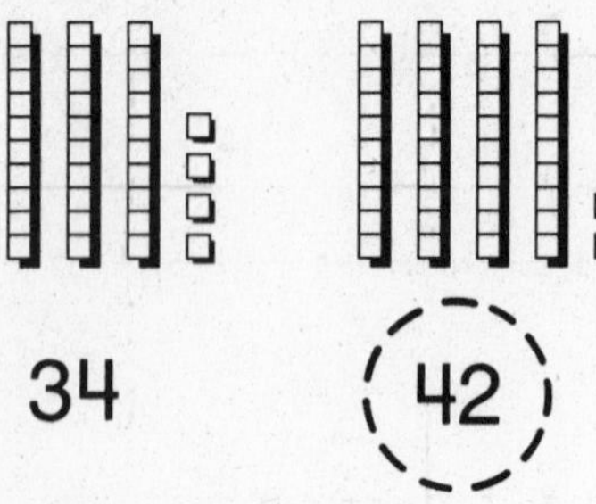

34 (42)

2. Ring the number that is less.

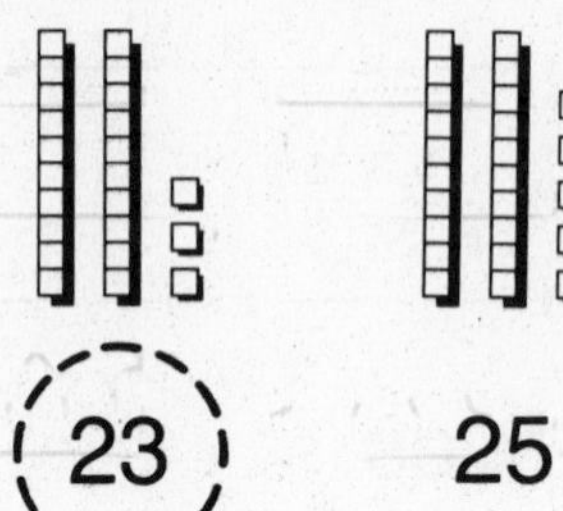

(23) 25

Ring the number that is greater.

3.	(15)	3	25	56	39	21
4.	50	60	79	96	42	39
5.	75	71	86	82	19	21
6.	64	67	34	43	56	50

Ring the number that is less.

7.	(5)	9	12	24	34	21
8.	29	19	82	74	63	69
9.	71	80	39	37	21	16
10.	61	54	25	45	91	89

Name

GRAPHING

Tickets Sold

Lucy	🎫	🎫	🎫	🎫		
Ed	🎫	🎫	🎫			
Irene	🎫	🎫	🎫	🎫	🎫	🎫
Jerry	🎫	🎫	🎫	🎫	🎫	

1. How many 🎫 did Lucy sell? 4
2. How many 🎫 did Jerry sell? 5
3. How many 🎫 did Ed sell? 3
4. How many 🎫 did Irene sell? 6
5. Who sold the most 🎫? Irene

Ring.

6. Who sold more 🎫? Jerry Lucy
7. Who sold more 🎫? Jerry (Irene)

Macmillan/McGraw-Hill, MATHEMATICS IN ACTION
Grade 1, Chapter 6, Lesson 14, pages 191–192

Name

PROBLEM SOLVING: USING INFORMATION FROM A GRAPH

Color to complete the graph.
Then use it to solve each problem.

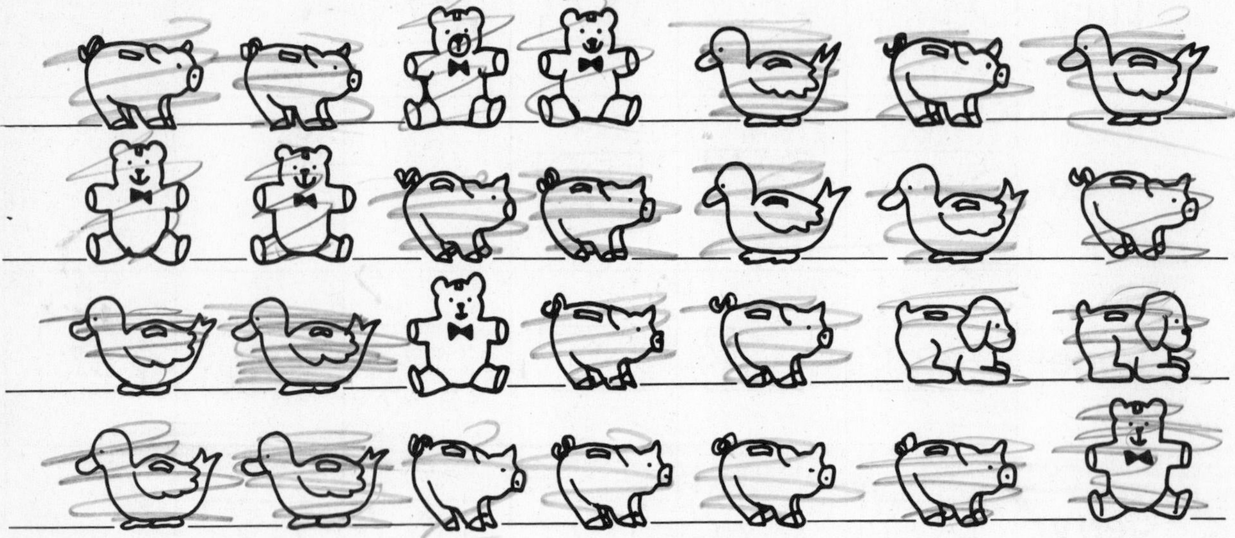

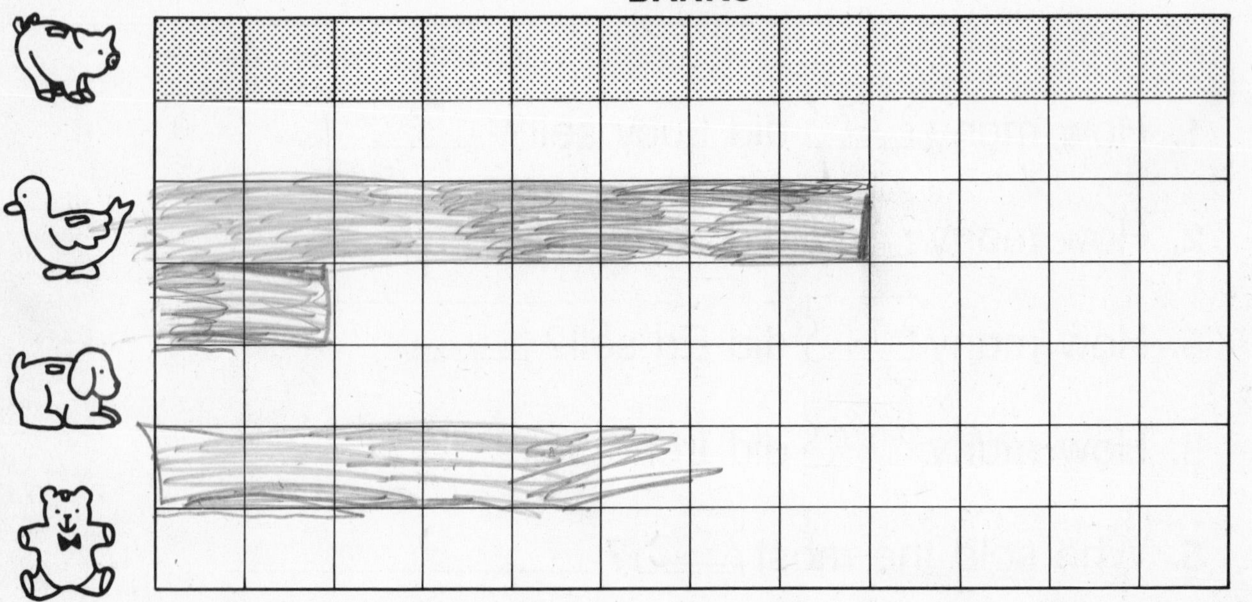

MACMILLAN/McGRAW-HILL

How many?

1.  12

2.  7

3.  2

4.  5

Name

PENNIES AND NICKELS

Show.	Write how much.	Show.	Write how much.
1. 8	8 ¢	2. 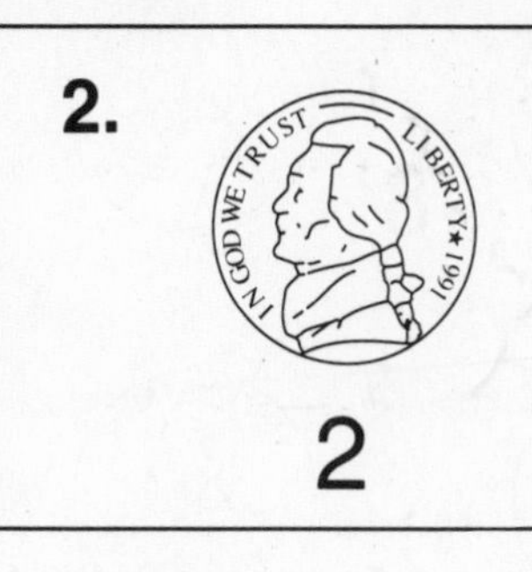 2	2 ¢
3. 10	10 ¢	4.  4 1	5 ¢
5.  1 2	3 ¢	6.   3 3	6 ¢
7.  1 5	6 ¢	8.  2 4	6 ¢
9.  1 7	8 ¢	10.  4 2	6 ¢

Name

PENNIES, NICKELS, AND DIMES

Show the coins.
Write how much.

1. 2  8  28¢

2. 3  6  ____¢

3. 1   2  ____¢

4. 3   1  ____¢

5. Carol has 1  and 4 . ____¢

6. Sam has 2  and 5 . ____¢

7. Kim has 2  and 3 . ____¢

Name

QUARTERS

1.

2.

3.

4.

5.

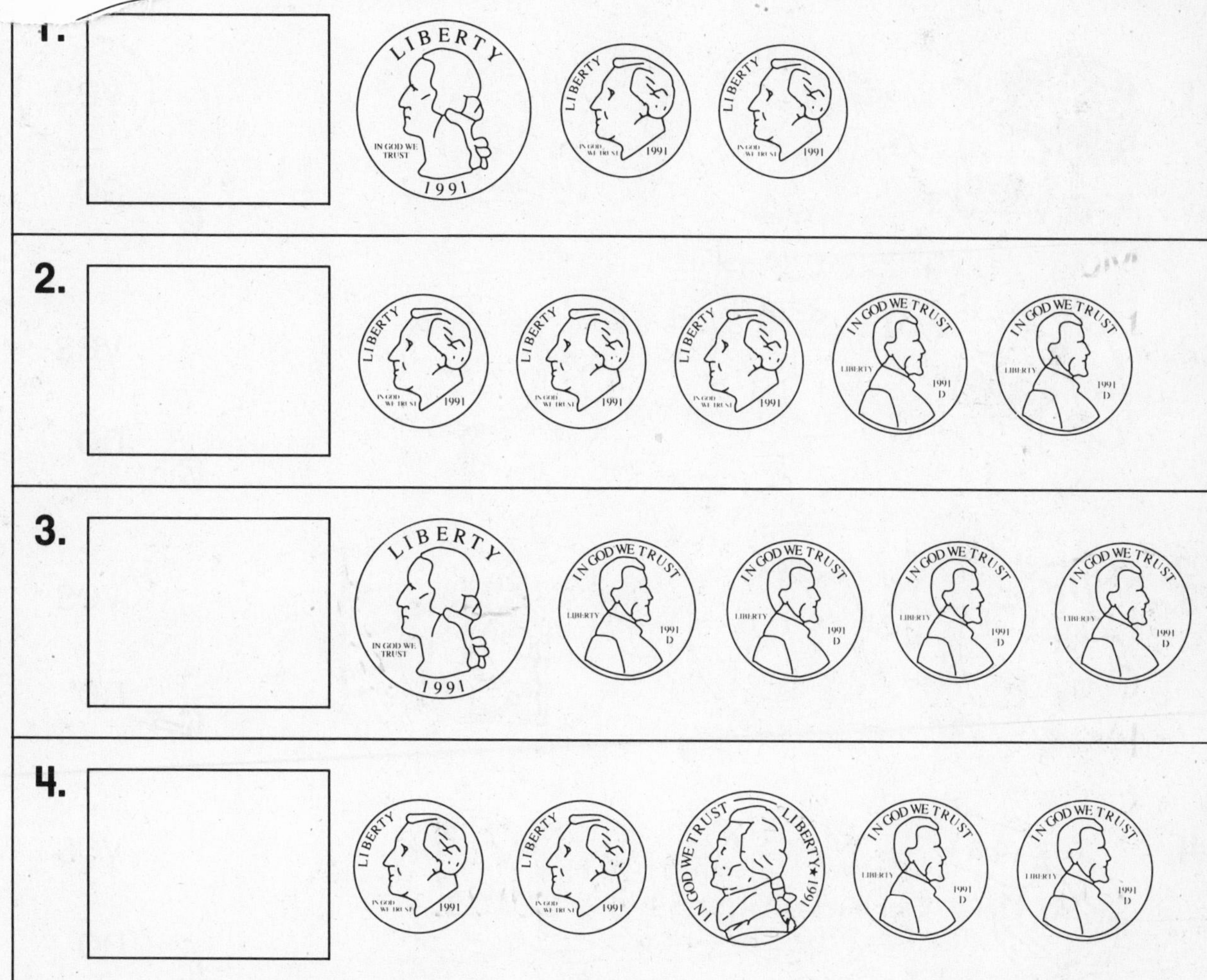

Macmillan/McGraw-Hill, MATHEMATICS IN ACTION
Grade 1, Chapter 7, Lesson 7, pages 217–218

Name

Coins

Write how much money you have.
Do you have enough?

1\. 

____¢ no

2\. 

____¢ yes no

3\. 

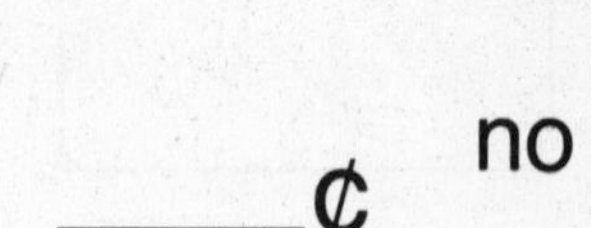

____¢ yes no

4\. 

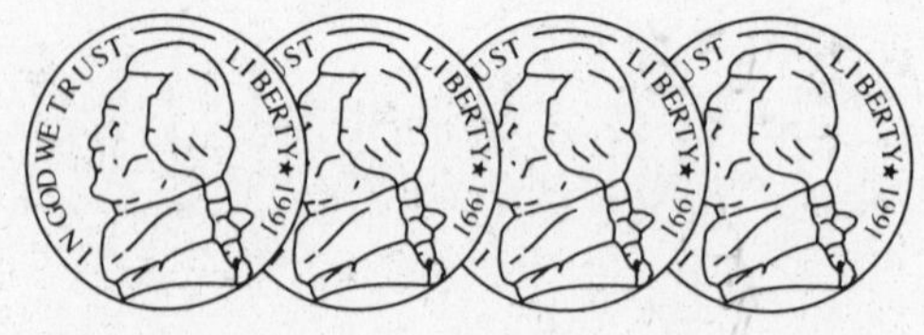

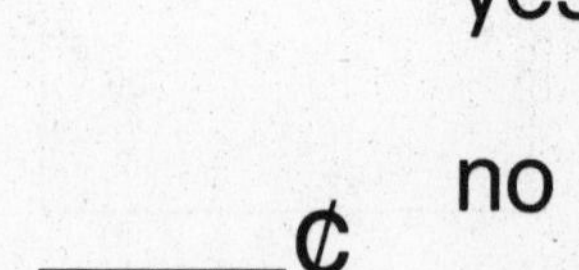

____¢ yes no

5\. 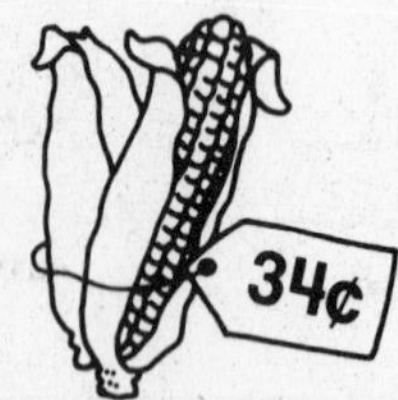

____¢ yes no

6\. 

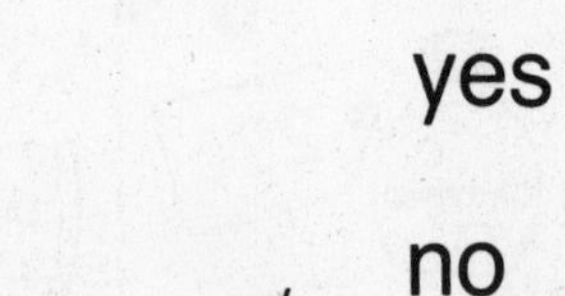

____¢ yes no

Macmillan/McGraw-Hill, MATHEMATICS IN ACTION
Grade 1, Chapter 7, Lesson 8, pages 219–220

Name

PROBLEM SOLVING STRATEGY: GUESS AND TEST

Ring 3 things each child can buy.
Guess and test.

1. Cleo spends $5.

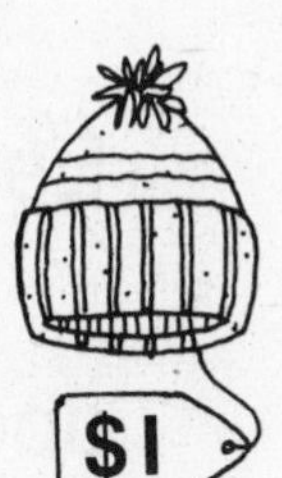

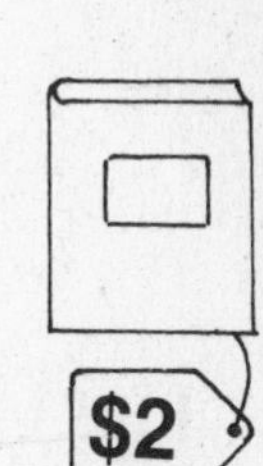

2. Frank spends $8.

3. Don spends $6.

4. Lois spends $7.

5. Jack spends $10.

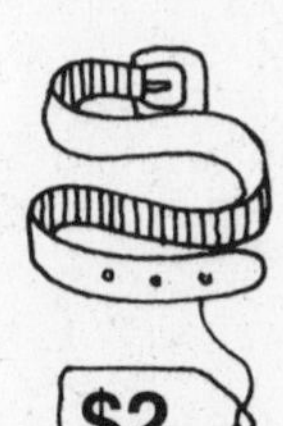

Macmillan/McGraw-Hill, MATHEMATICS IN ACTION
Grade 1, Chapter 7, Lesson 9, pages 221–222

Name

CENTIMETERS AND DECIMETERS

Estimate how long.
Then use your centimeter to measure.

	Estimate	Measure
1. 	about ____ cm	about __4__ cm
2. 	about ____ cm	about ____ cm
3. 	about ____ cm	about ____ cm

Measure how long.

 4. 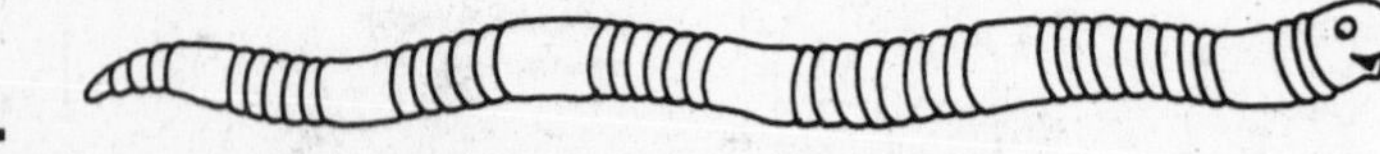 about ____ cm

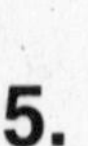 5.  about ____ cm

 6.  about ____ cm

 7.  about ____ cm

 8. 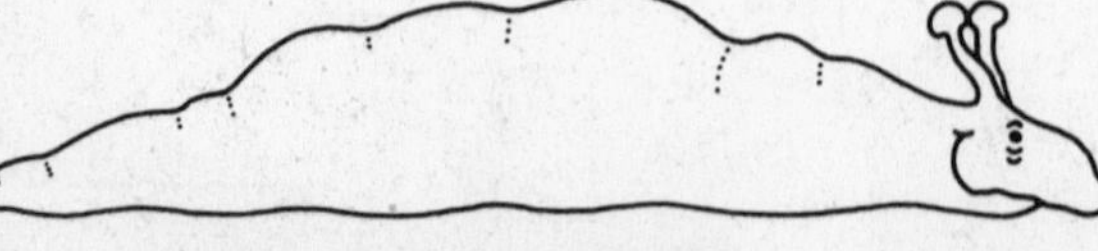 about ____ cm

Name

LITER

Color the containers.

about 1 liter

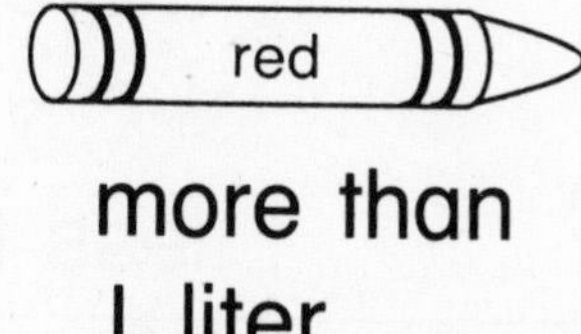

more than 1 liter

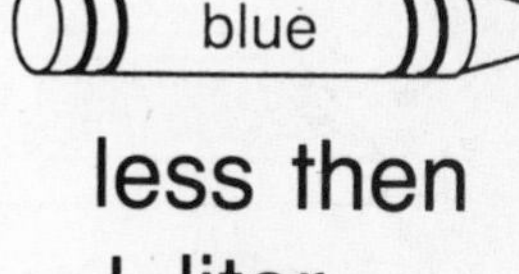

less then 1 liter

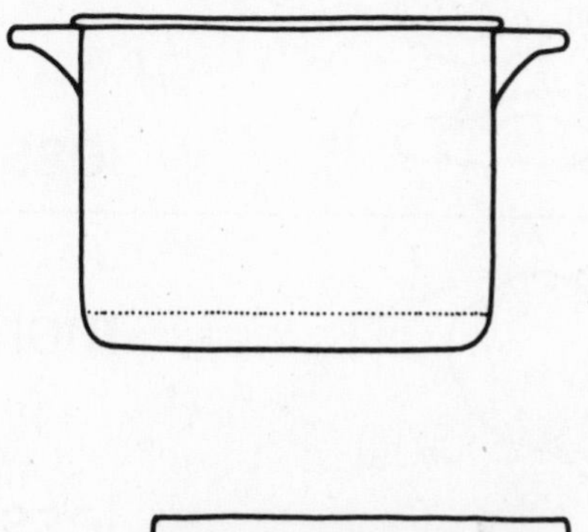

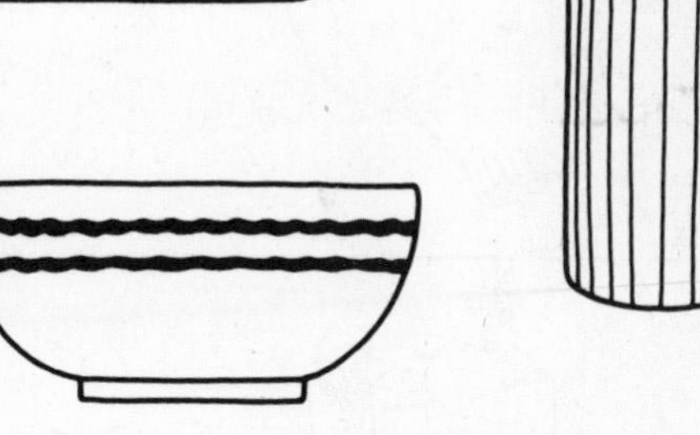

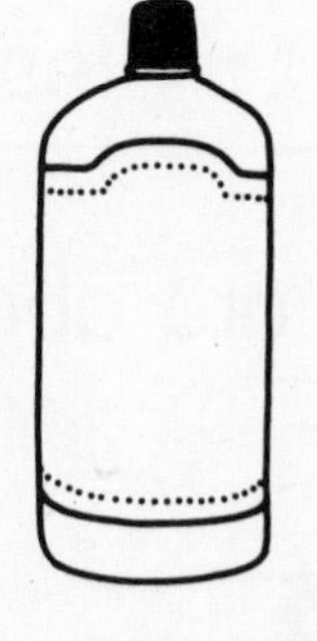

Name

KILOGRAM

Ring the better estimate.

1. 
more than 1 kilogram
less than 1 kilogram

2. 
more than 1 kilogram
less than 1 kilogram

3. 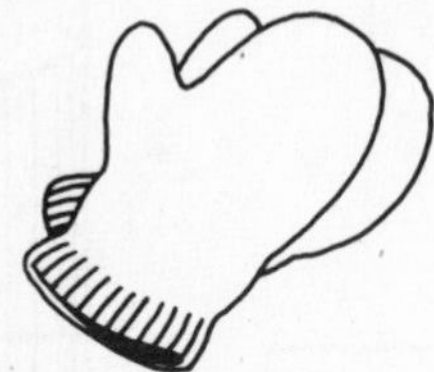
more than 1 kilogram
less than 1 kilogram

4. 
more than 1 kilogram
less than 1 kilogram

Ring the objects that are about 1 kilogram.

5.     

Name

PROBLEM SOLVING STRATEGY: USING ESTIMATION

Draw lines to match each toy to the best box.

1.

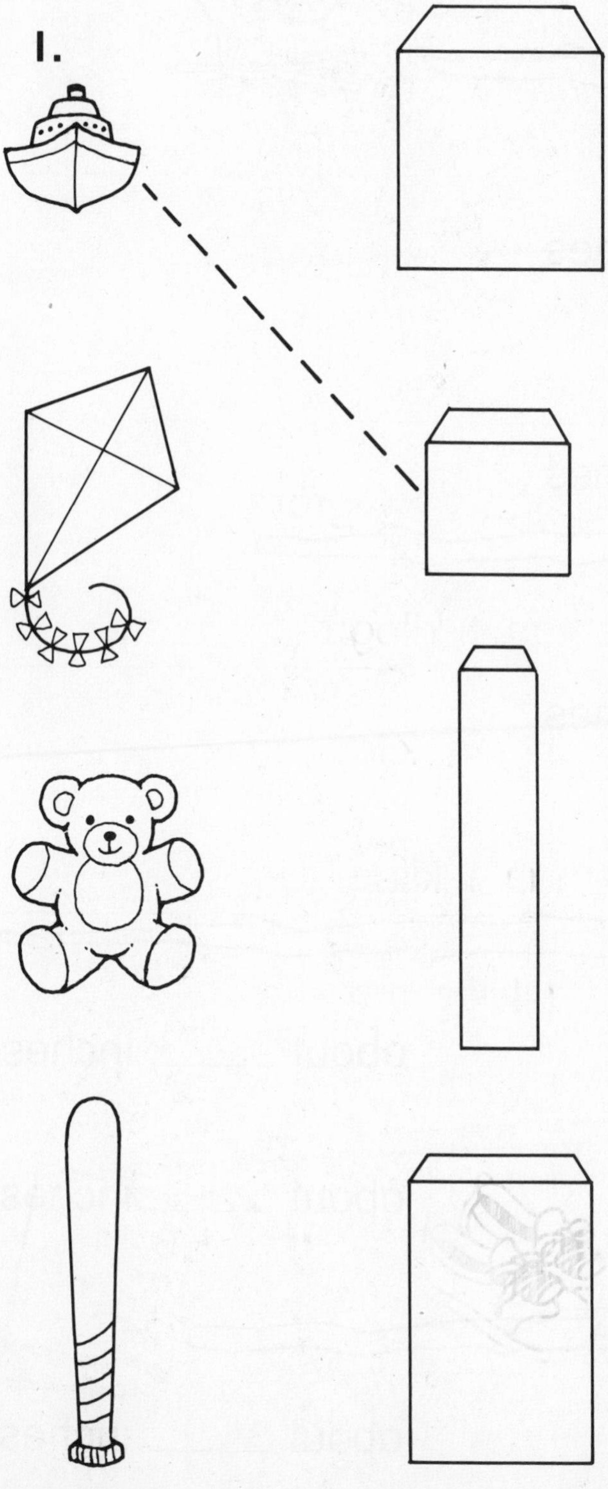

2.

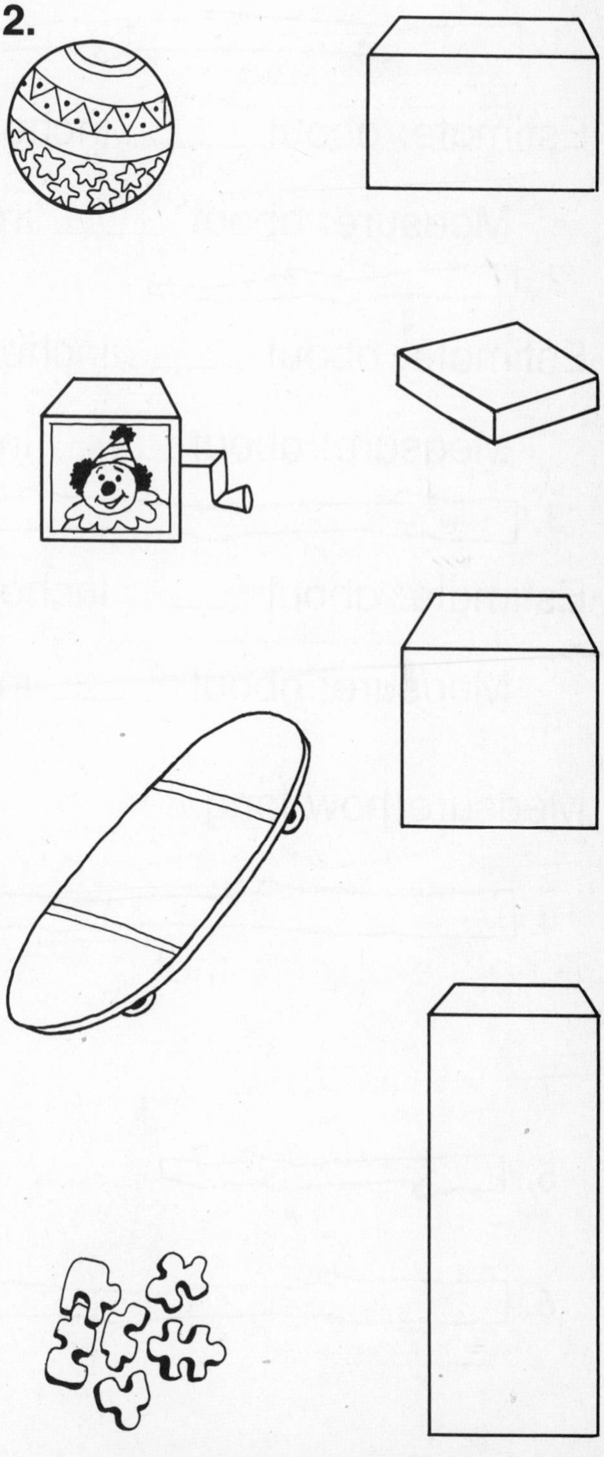

Macmillan/McGraw-Hill, MATHEMATICS IN ACTION
Grade 1, Chapter 8, Lesson 6, pages 241–242

Name

INCH AND FOOT

Estimate how long.
Then use your [inch ruler] to measure.

1.

Estimate: about _____ inches

Measure: about _____ inches

2.

Estimate: about _____ inches

Measure: about _____ inches

3.

Estimate: about _____ inches

Measure: about _____ inches

Measure how long.

4. 

about _____ inches

5. about _____ inches

6.

about _____ inches

Name

CUP, PINT, AND QUART

Ring how much it can hold.

1.  more than 1 cup   less than 1 cup

2.  more than 1 cup   less than 1 cup

3. 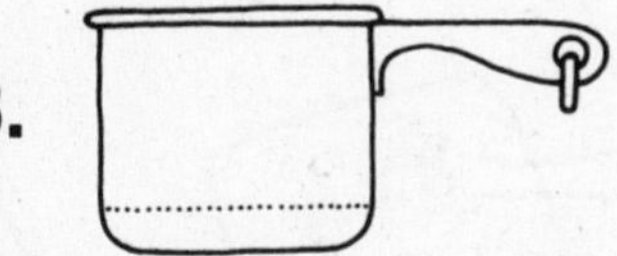 more than 1 pint   less than 1 pint

4.  more than 1 pint   less than 1 pint

5.  more than 1 quart   less than 1 quart

6.  more than 1 quart   less than 1 quart

7. 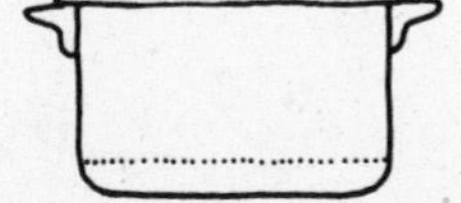 more than 1 quart   less than 1 quart

Macmillan/McGraw-Hill, MATHEMATICS IN ACTION
Grade 1, Chapter 8, Lesson 9, page 247

Name

POUND

Color.

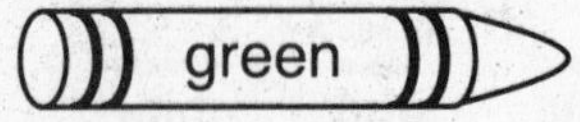

more than 1 pound

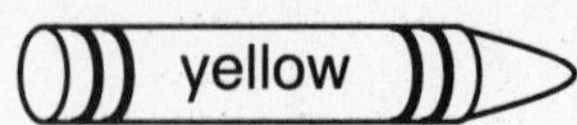

less than 1 pound

XXX
FLOUR

MACMILLAN/McGRAW-HILL

Name

TEMPERATURE

Color to show the temperature.

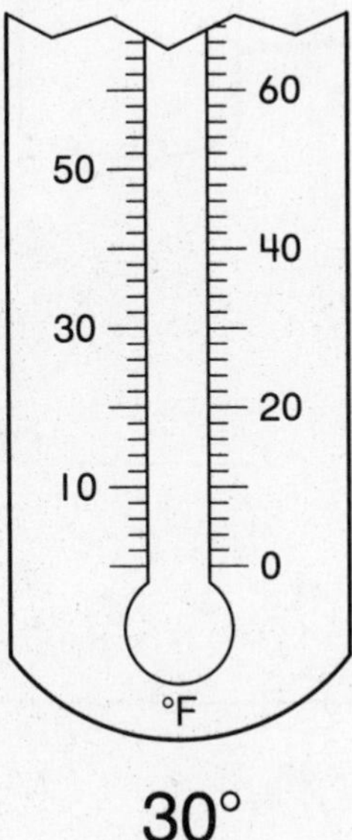

30°

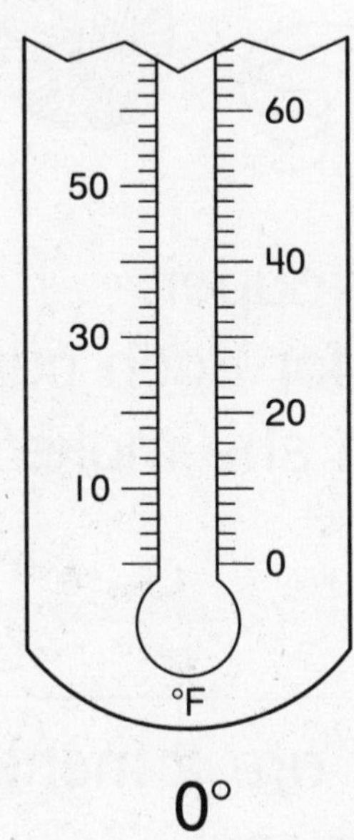

0°

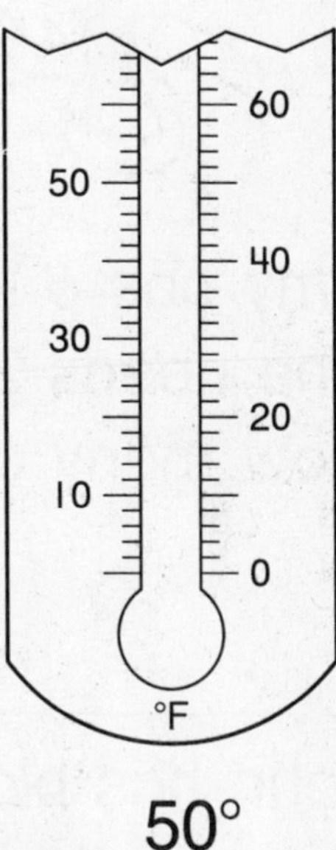

50°

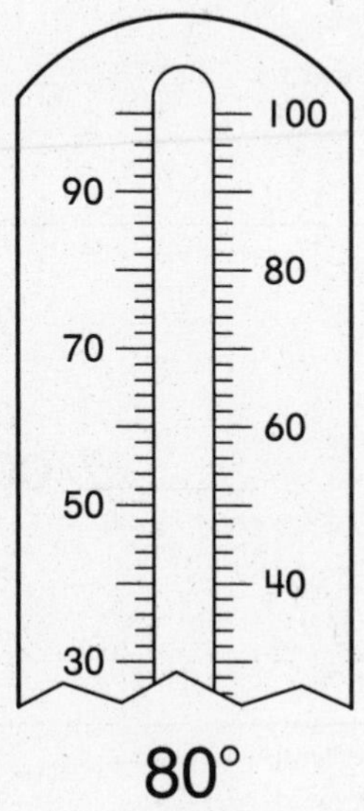

80°

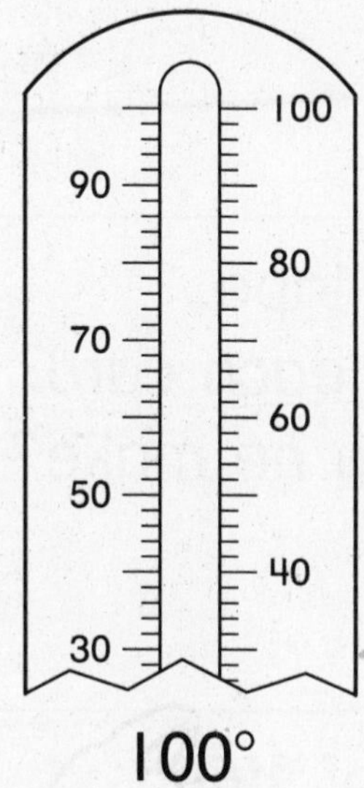

100°

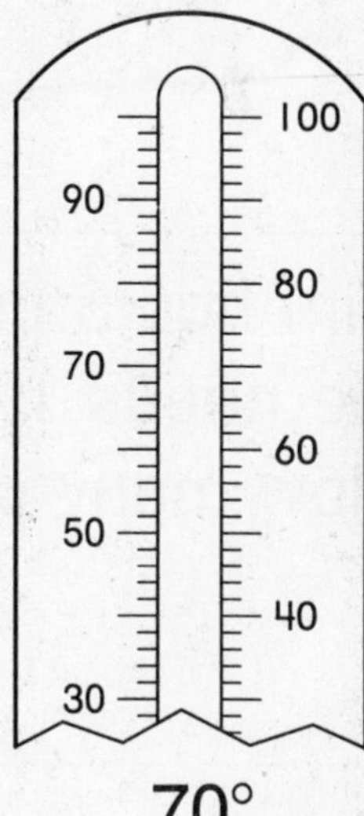

70°

Macmillan/McGraw-Hill, MATHEMATICS IN ACTION
Grade 1, Chapter 8, Lesson 11, pages 249–250

Name

PROBLEM SOLVING STRATEGY: DRAWING A PICTURE

Draw a picture to solve.

1. Amy has 6 inches of paper.
   She needs 2 inches for each card.
   How many cards can she make? _____ cards

2. John has blocks that are 2 inches long.
   He puts 2 blocks in a row.
   How long is the row of blocks? _____ inches

3. Tim has 3 inches of tape.
   He needs 1 inch for each card.
   How many cards can he make? _____ cards

4. Carol has 6 inches of string.
   She needs 3 inches for each hook.
   How many hooks can she make? _____ hooks

Name

SUMS AND DIFFERENCES TO 11

Write an addition fact and a subtraction fact.

1.

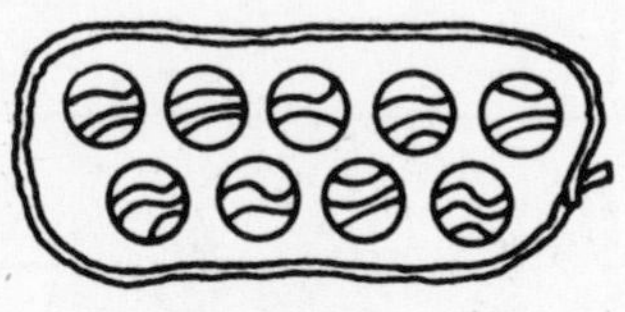
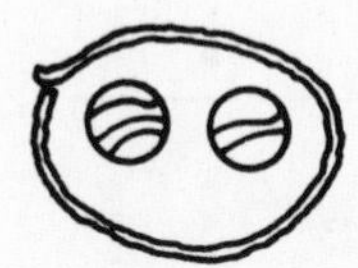

9 2

9 + 2 = 11

11 − 2 = 9

2.

4 7

___ + ___ = 11

11 − ___ = 4

3.

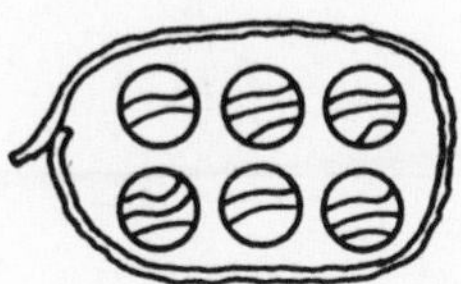

5 6

___ + ___ = 11

11 − ___ = ___

4.

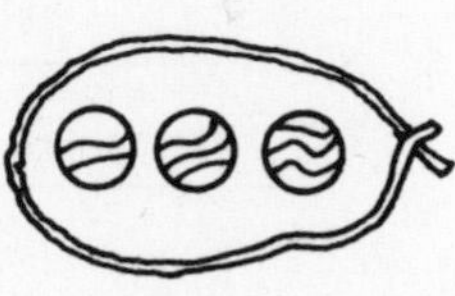

3 8

___ + ___ = 11

11 − ___ = ___

5.

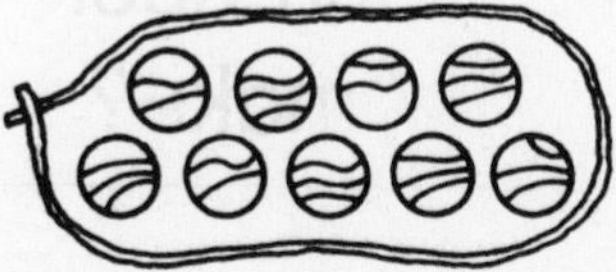

2 9

___ + ___ = 11

11 − ___ = ___

Macmillan/McGraw-Hill, MATHEMATICS IN ACTION
Grade 1, Chapter 9, Lesson 2, pages 265–266

Name

MORE SUMS AND DIFFERENCES TO 11

Write the fact family.

1.

6 + 5 = 11 | 11 − 5 = 6

5 + 6 = 11 | 11 − 6 = 5

2.

3.

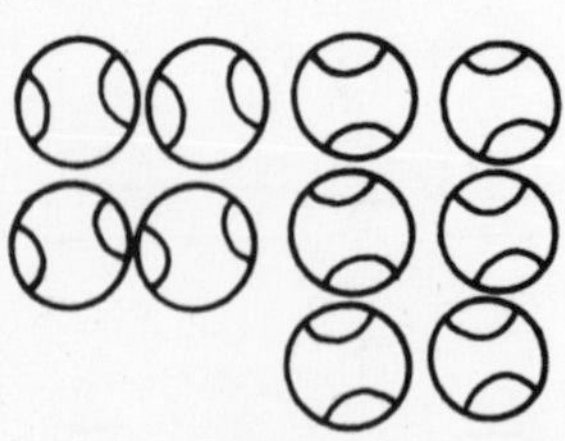

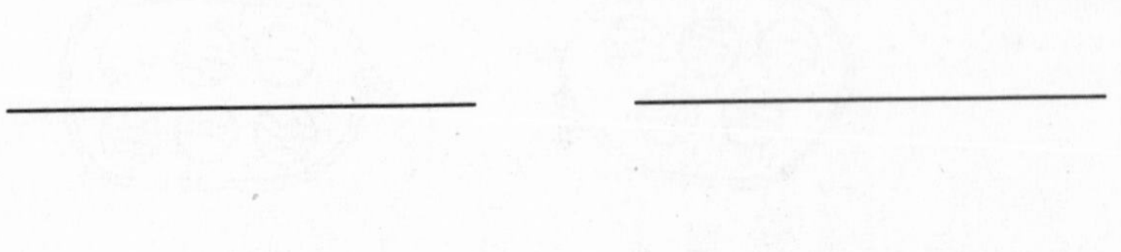

4.

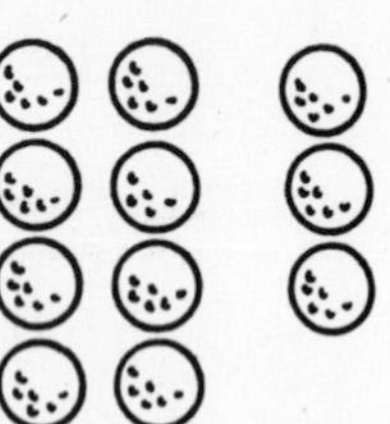

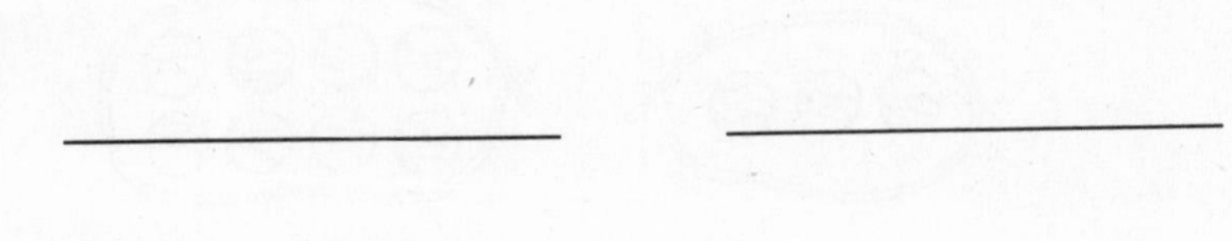

5.

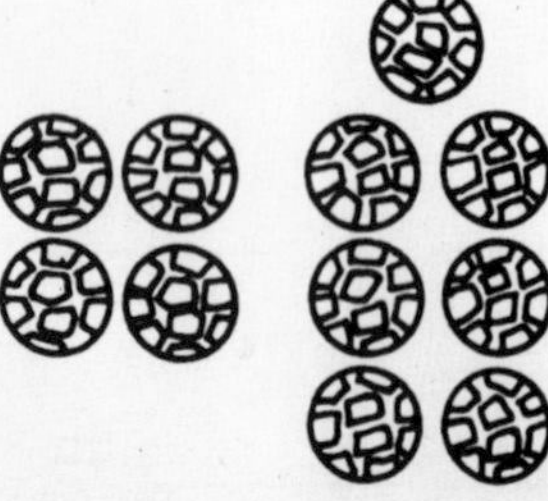

Name

PROBLEM SOLVING STRATEGY: CHOOSING THE OPERATION

Decide when to add.
Decide when to subtract.
Solve.

1. Luke found 11 shells.
   He gave 5 shells to Jane.
   How many does he have left? _____ shells

2. Eva caught 4 fish.
   Charlie caught 7 fish.
   How many fish did they catch? _____ fish

3. Darcy saw 9 crabs.
   4 crabs ran away.
   How many crabs are left? _____ crabs

4. Lee found 6 white rocks.
   He found 4 grey rocks.
   How many rocks did he find? _____ rocks

5. Della found 9 starfish.
   She threw 9 starfish back
   in the water.
   How many starfish are left? _____ starfish

6. Bob caught 11 snails.
   7 snails got away.
   How many snails are left? _____ snails

Macmillan/McGraw-Hill, MATHEMATICS IN ACTION
Grade 1, Chapter 9, Lesson 4, pages 269–270

Name

PROBLEM SOLVING STRATEGY: USING SUBTRACTION TO COMPARE

Solve.

1. Melba has 7 stickers.
   Jake has 10 stickers.
   How many more stickers
   does Jake have than Melba?  ______ more

2. Carl has 9 red toy cars.
   He has 5 blue toy cars.
   How many more red cars
   than blue cars does he have? ______ more

3. June made a necklace with
   11 green beads and 9 yellow beads.
   How many fewer yellow beads than
   green beads did she use? ______ fewer

4. Fred drew 10 pictures.
   Gene drew 6 pictures.
   How many more pictures did
   Fred draw than Gene? ______ more

5. Sue has 11 pencils.
   Lucy has 6 pencils.
   How many fewer pencils does
   Lucy have than Sue? ______ fewer

Name

SUMS AND DIFFERENCES TO 12

Write an addition fact and a subtraction fact.

1. 8 + 4 = 12 12 − 4 = 8

2. ____ + ____ = 12 12 − ____ = ____

3. ____ + ____ = 12 12 − ____ = ____

4. ____ + ____ = 12 12 − ____ = ____

5. ____ + ____ = 12 12 − ____ = ____

6. ____ + ____ = 12 12 − ____ = ____

7. ____ + ____ = 12 12 − ____ = ____

Name

MORE SUMS AND DIFFERENCES TO 12

Add.

1. $\begin{array}{r} 6 \\ +6 \\ \hline 12 \end{array}$ $\begin{array}{r} 5 \\ +7 \\ \hline \end{array}$ $\begin{array}{r} 4 \\ +8 \\ \hline \end{array}$ $\begin{array}{r} 8 \\ +3 \\ \hline \end{array}$ $\begin{array}{r} 4 \\ +7 \\ \hline \end{array}$ $\begin{array}{r} 3 \\ +9 \\ \hline \end{array}$

2. $\begin{array}{r} 7 \\ +5 \\ \hline \end{array}$ $\begin{array}{r} 9 \\ +2 \\ \hline \end{array}$ $\begin{array}{r} 6 \\ +5 \\ \hline \end{array}$ $\begin{array}{r} 8 \\ +4 \\ \hline \end{array}$ $\begin{array}{r} 7 \\ +3 \\ \hline \end{array}$ $\begin{array}{r} 3 \\ +8 \\ \hline \end{array}$

Subtract.

3. $\begin{array}{r} 12 \\ -4 \\ \hline 8 \end{array}$ $\begin{array}{r} 12 \\ -9 \\ \hline \end{array}$ $\begin{array}{r} 9 \\ -6 \\ \hline \end{array}$ $\begin{array}{r} 12 \\ -7 \\ \hline \end{array}$ $\begin{array}{r} 10 \\ -3 \\ \hline \end{array}$ $\begin{array}{r} 11 \\ -8 \\ \hline \end{array}$

4. $\begin{array}{r} 9 \\ -4 \\ \hline \end{array}$ $\begin{array}{r} 12 \\ -8 \\ \hline \end{array}$ $\begin{array}{r} 8 \\ -8 \\ \hline \end{array}$ $\begin{array}{r} 12 \\ -3 \\ \hline \end{array}$ $\begin{array}{r} 10 \\ -5 \\ \hline \end{array}$ $\begin{array}{r} 12 \\ -5 \\ \hline \end{array}$

Write the fact family.

5. ____________ ____________

____________ ____________

Name

ADDING AND SUBTRACTING MONEY

Add or subtract.
Color.

12 red	11 yellow
10 green	6 purple
5 blue	4 orange

4¢ + 7¢ = 11¢	12¢ − 8¢	10¢ − 5¢	6¢ + 6¢	7¢ + 4¢
9¢ + 1¢	8¢ − 3¢	12¢ − 6¢	11¢ − 7¢	8¢ + 2¢
11¢ − 6¢	8¢ + 4¢	6¢ + 5¢	5¢ + 5¢	11¢ − 6¢
11¢ − 5¢	10¢ − 6¢	7¢ + 3¢	12¢ − 7¢	3¢ + 9¢
9¢ + 3¢	3¢ + 8¢	4¢ + 8¢	8¢ + 3¢	10¢ − 4¢

Name

THREE ADDENDS

Add. Use cubes to help.

1.

4	5	2	1
5	4	5	5
+ 3	+ 1	+ 2	+ 6
12			

2.

5	5	3	1
3	1	3	4
+ 1	+ 5	+ 4	+ 7

3.

6	3	8	1
2	2	1	3
+ 1	+ 5	+ 3	+ 5

4.

4	2	6	5
1	1	2	4
+ 3	+ 7	+ 4	+ 3

Name

Hour

Match the clocks that show the same time.

I. 

10:00

2. 

7:00

3. 

2:00

4. 

3:00

5. 

11:00

6. 

6:00

Name

MORE ABOUT TIME TO THE HOUR

Write the time.

1. 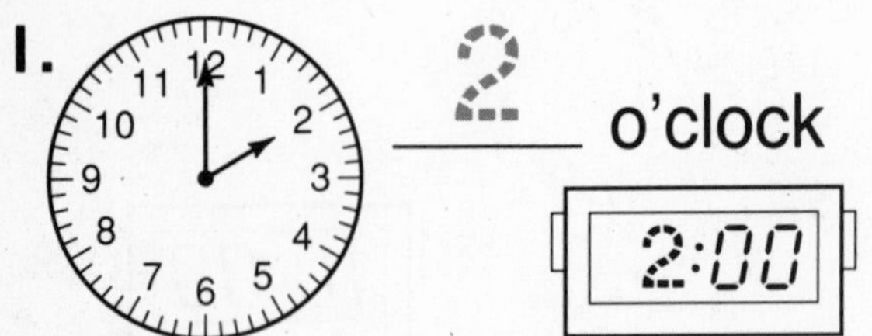

2. 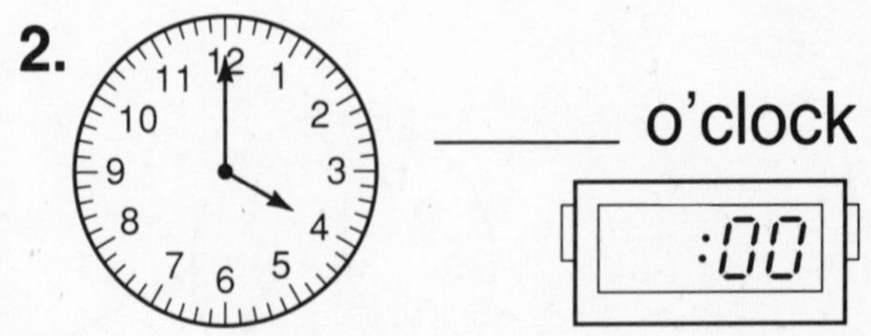

3. 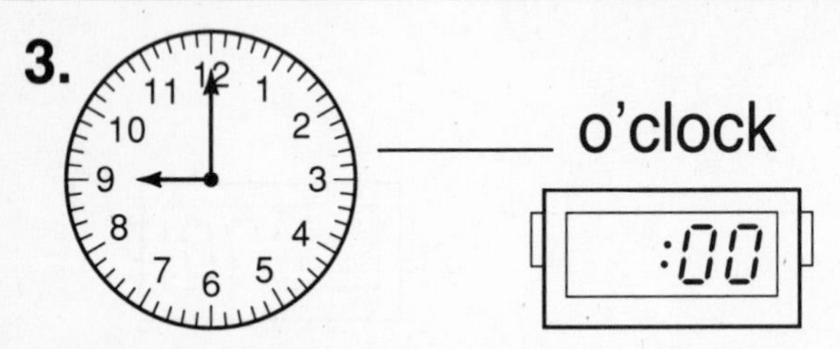

4. 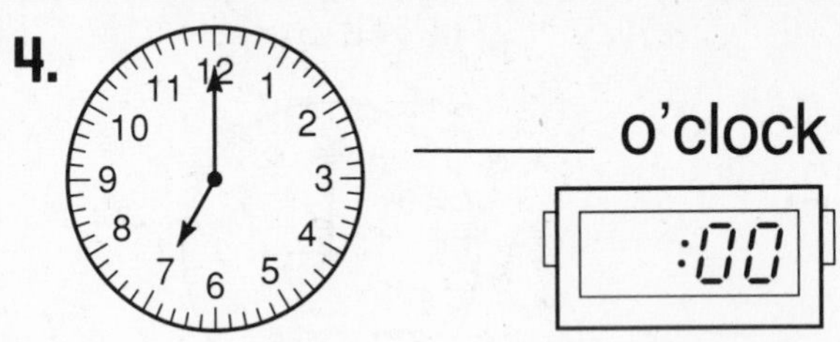

5. 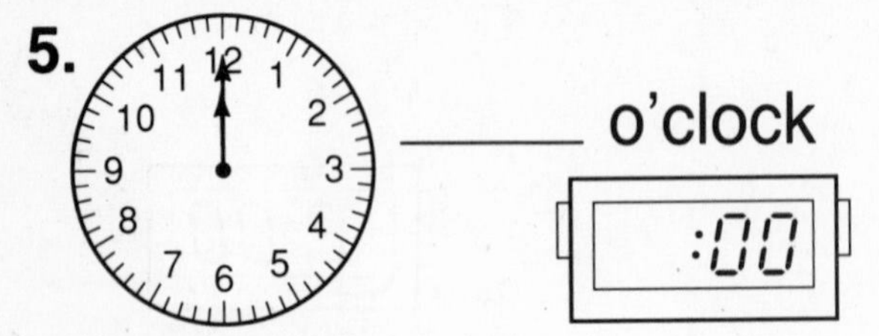

6. 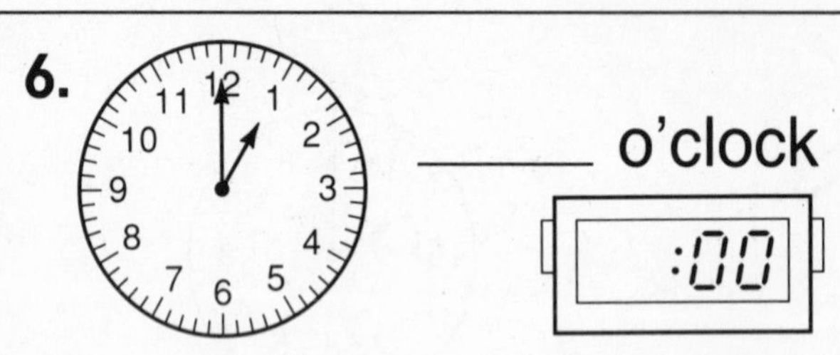

7. 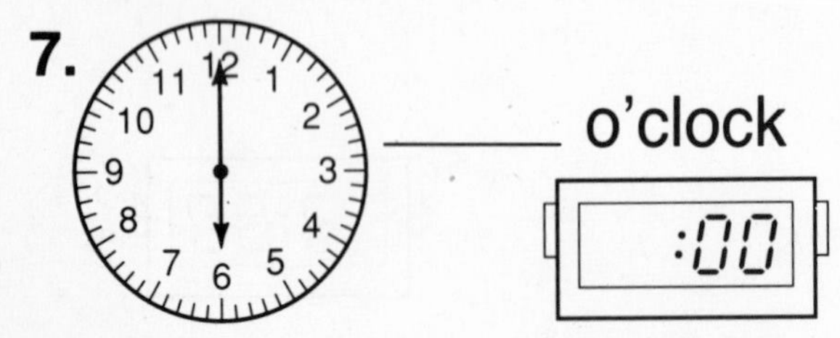

8. 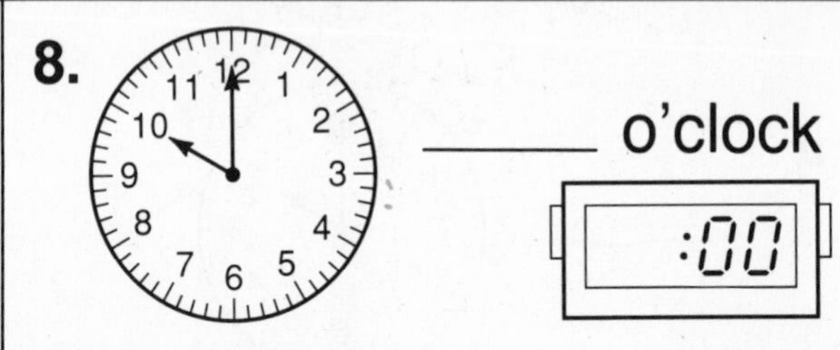

9. 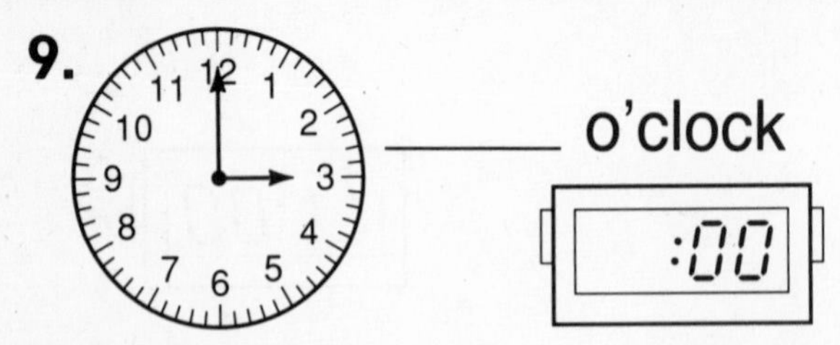

10. 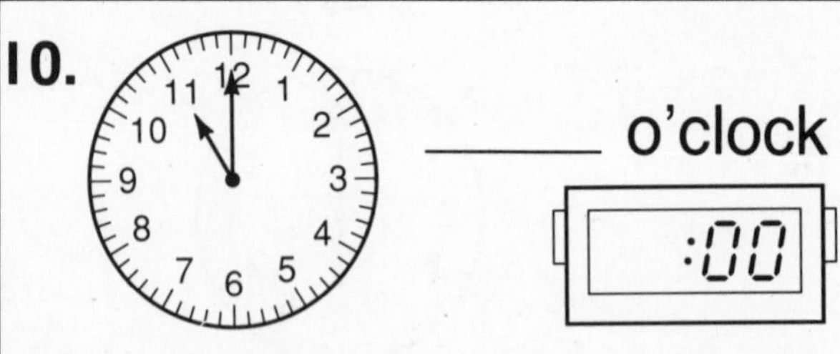

11. 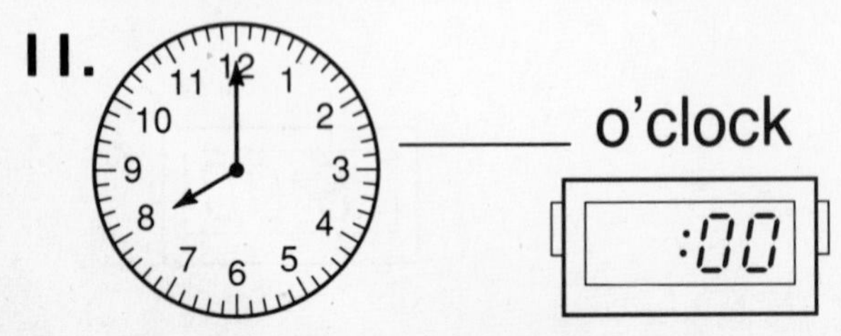

12. 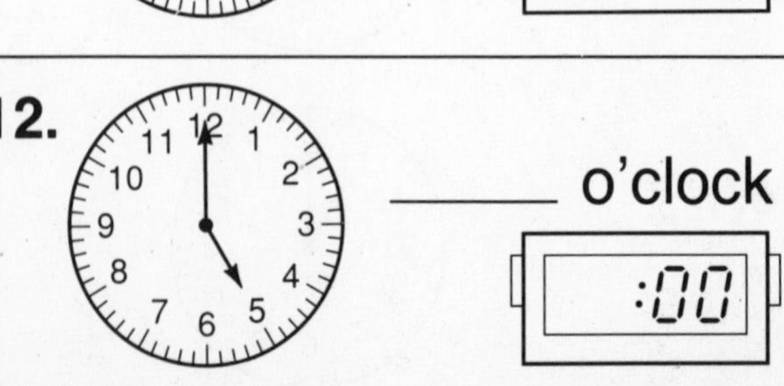

Name

PROBLEM SOLVING STRATEGY: MAKING A LIST

Betty has these clothes.

How many different outfits can she make?
Color to show the different outfits.

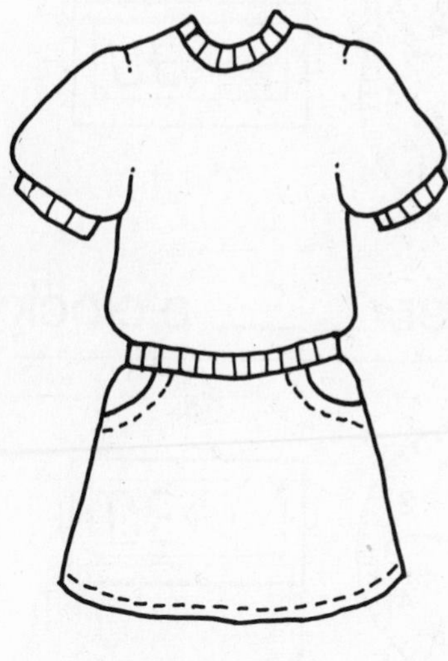
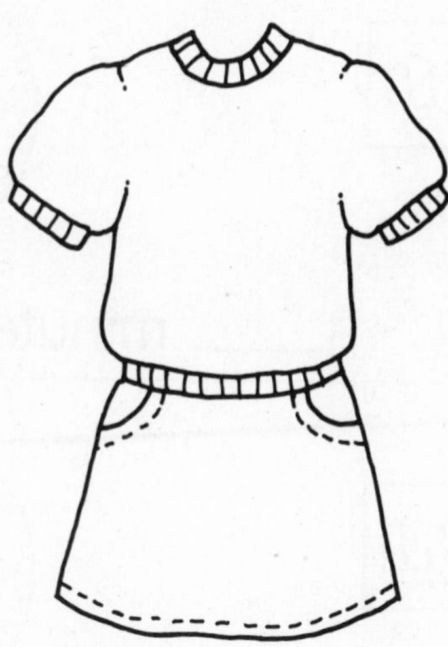
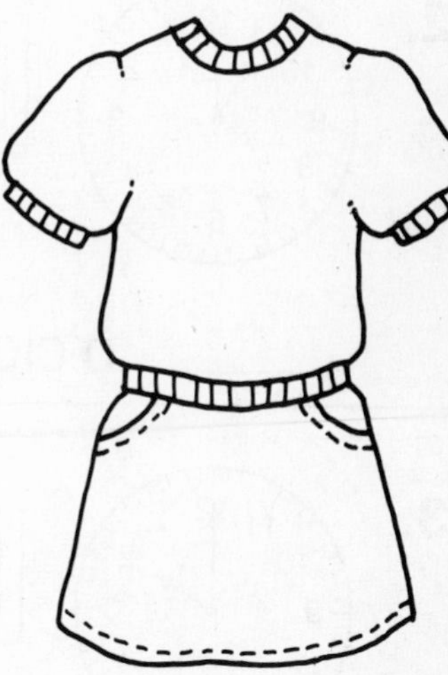

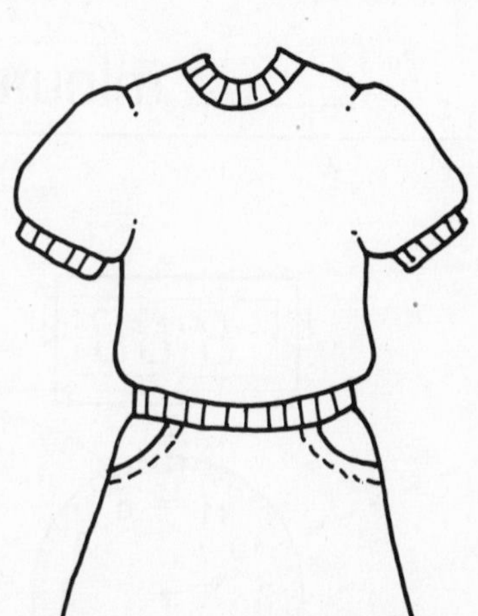

Name

HALF HOUR

Write the times.

1. 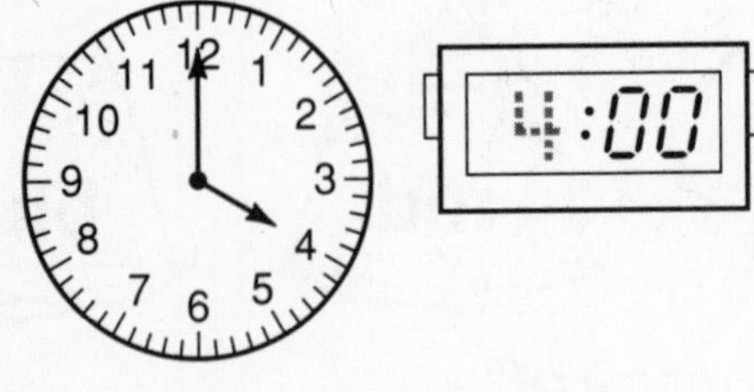

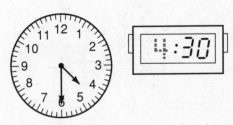

4 o'clock 30 minutes after 4 o'clock

2. 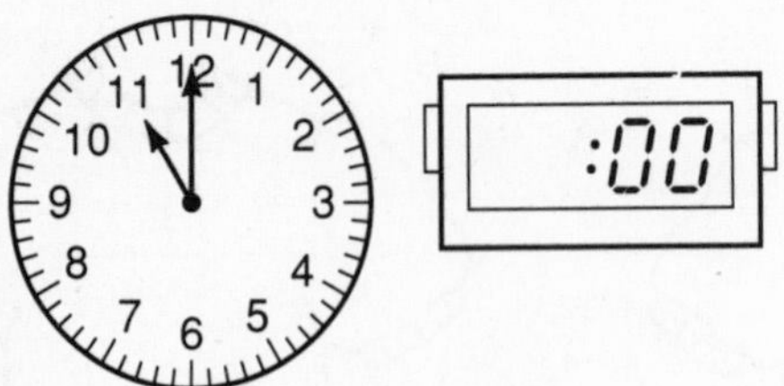

_____ o'clock _____ minutes after _____ o'clock

3. 

_____ o'clock _____ minutes after _____ o'clock

Match.

4. 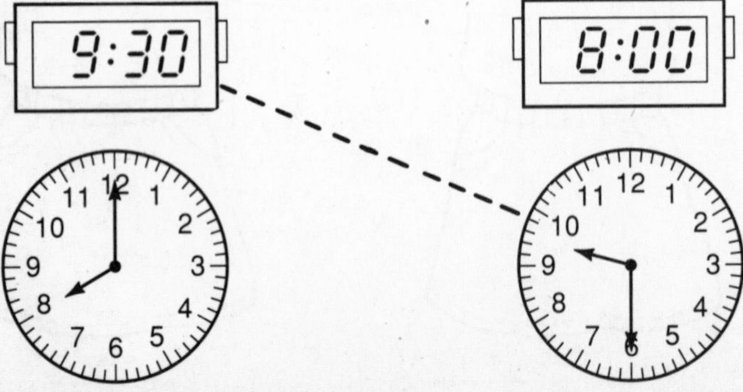

6:30

MACMILLAN/McGRAW-HILL

Name

MORE ABOUT TIME TO THE HALF HOUR

Draw the minute hand.
Write the time.

1. 
2:30

2. 
:30

3. 

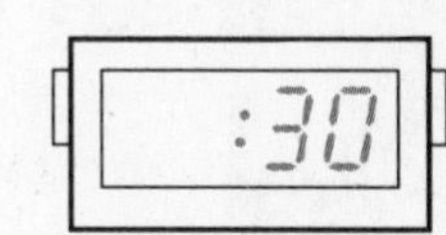

Write the time.

4. 

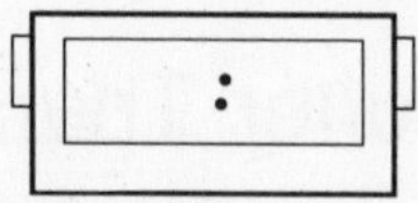

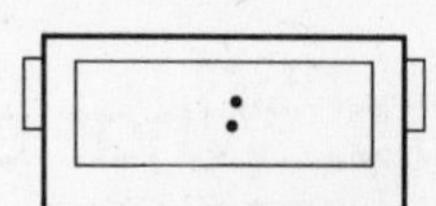

5. 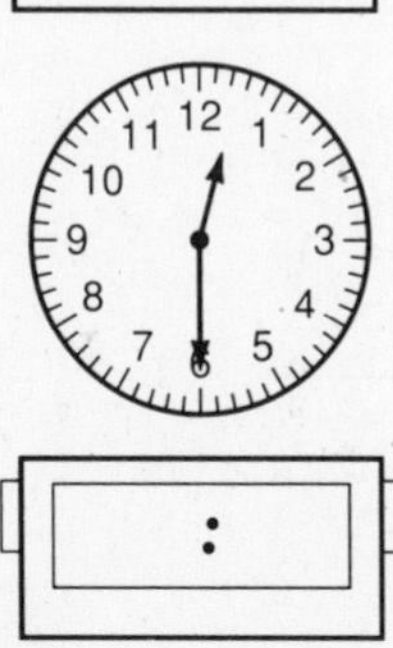

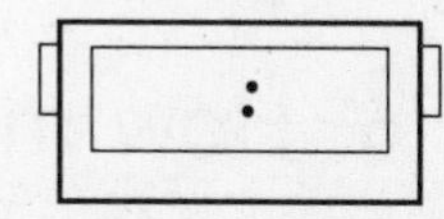

Name

DAYS OF THE WEEK

Complete the calendar. Answer the questions.

OCTOBER						
Sunday	Monday	Tuesday	Wednesday	Thursday	Friday	Saturday
		1				5
			9			
	14					
					25	
				31		

1. How many days in October? _____
2. How many Fridays? _____
3. What day comes after Thursday? ________
4. What day comes after Saturday? ________
5. How many school days in October? _____
6. How many weekend days? _____

Name

PROBLEM SOLVING STRATEGIES REVIEW

Solve.

1. Donna picked 12 flowers.
   She gave 3 flowers to Phil.
   How many flowers does she have left? _____ flowers

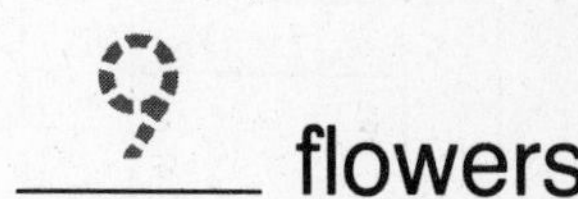

2. Lisa saw 5 bluebirds.
   Jerry saw 6 bluebirds.
   How many bluebirds did they see in all?
   _____ bluebirds

3. Billy picked 8 pails of berries.
   Joanne picked 6 pails of berries.
   How many more pails of berries did
   Billy pick than Joanne? _____ more

4. Sylvia is making price tags.
   She has 5 inches of paper.
   She needs 1 inch of paper for each
   price tag.
   How many price tags can she make? _____ price tags

5. Rose picked 5 tomatoes.
   Neil picked 7 tomatoes.
   How many tomatoes did they
   pick altogether? _____ tomatoes

Name

THREE-DIMENSIONAL FIGURES

Color the objects that have the same shape.

1. 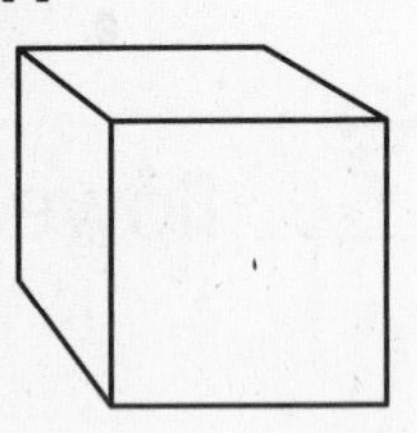  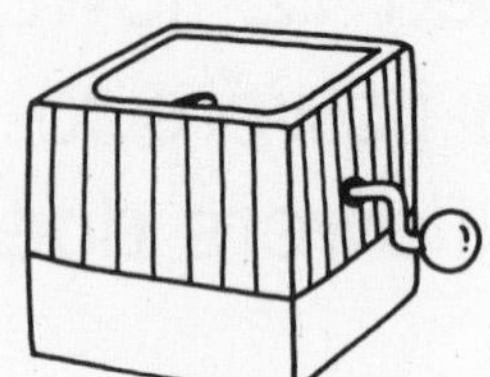 

2. 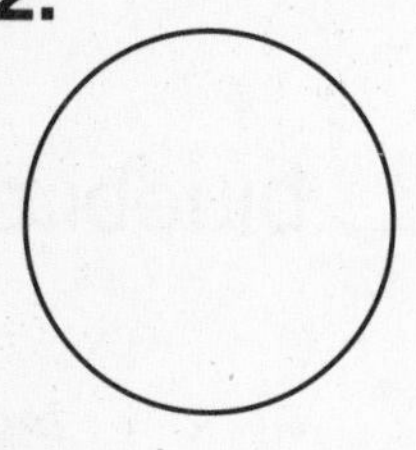   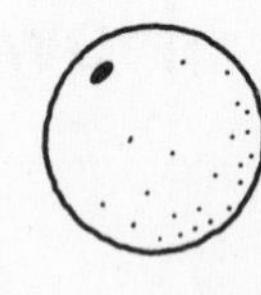

3. 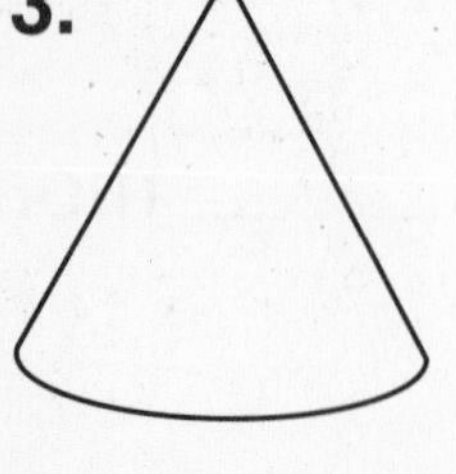  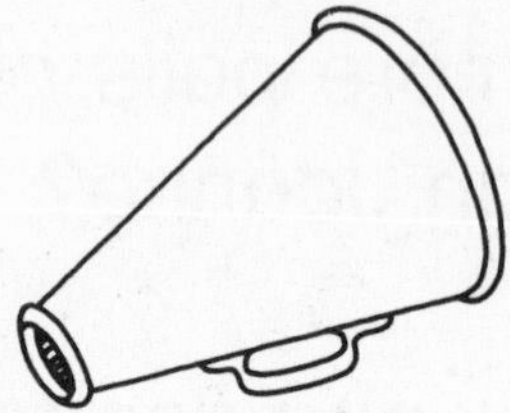 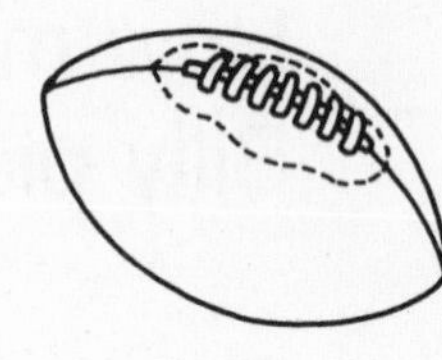

4. 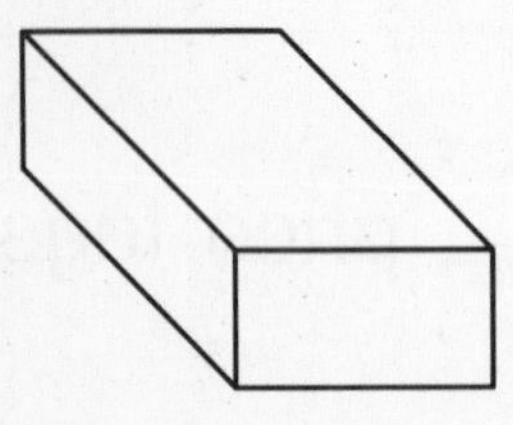 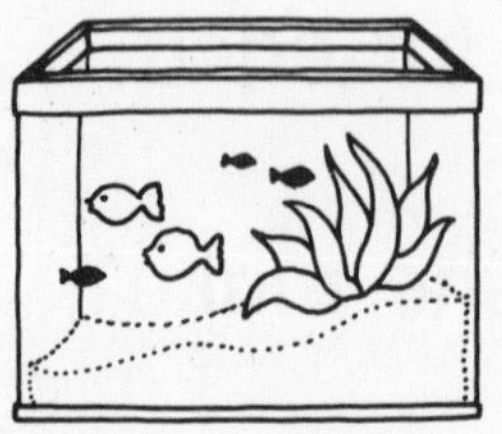 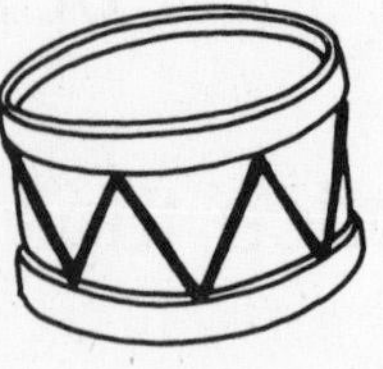 

5.  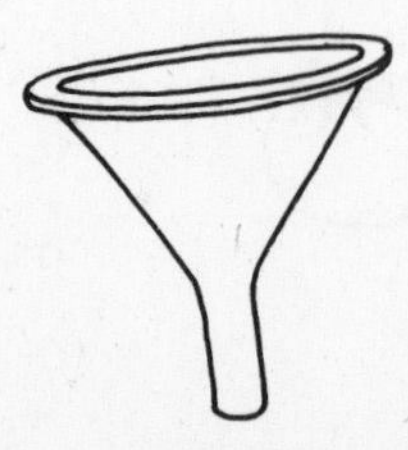  

Name

TWO-DIMENSIONAL FIGURES

Color inside the shapes.

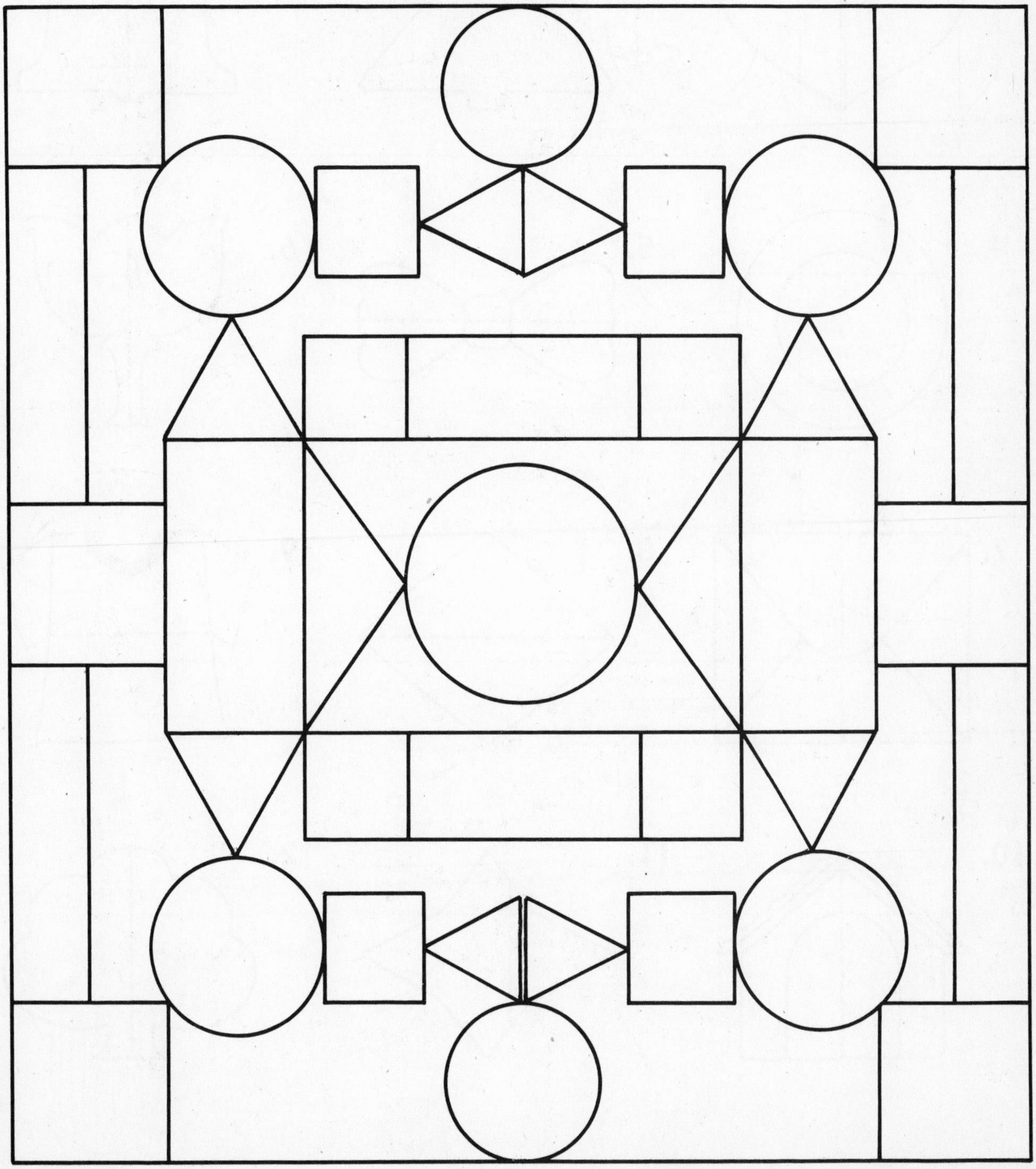

□ red
△ green
▯ blue
○ yellow

MACMILLAN/McGRAW-HILL

Macmillan/McGraw-Hill, MATHEMATICS IN ACTION
Grade 1, Chapter 11, Lesson 3, pages 325–326

Name

Symmetry

Color the shape if both parts match.

1. 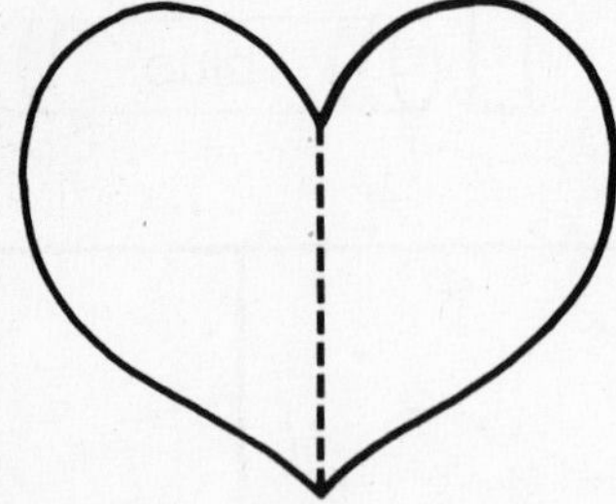

2. 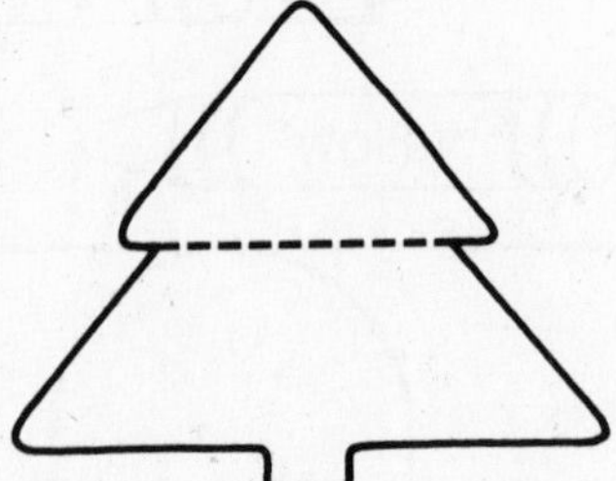

3. 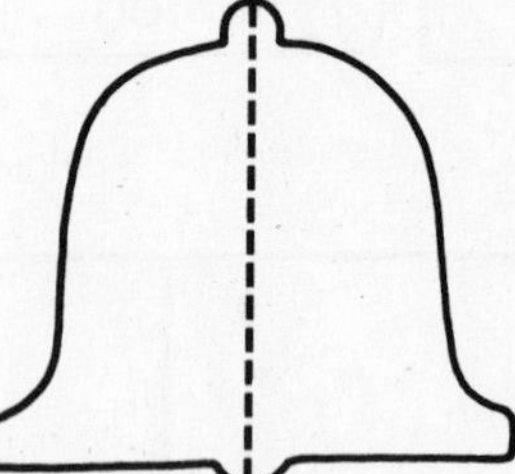

4. 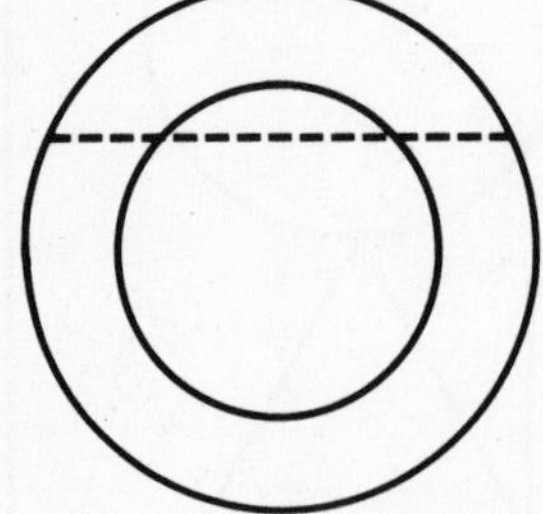

5. 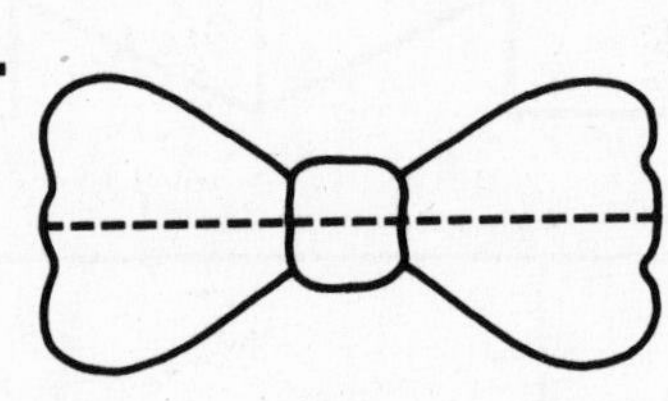

6. 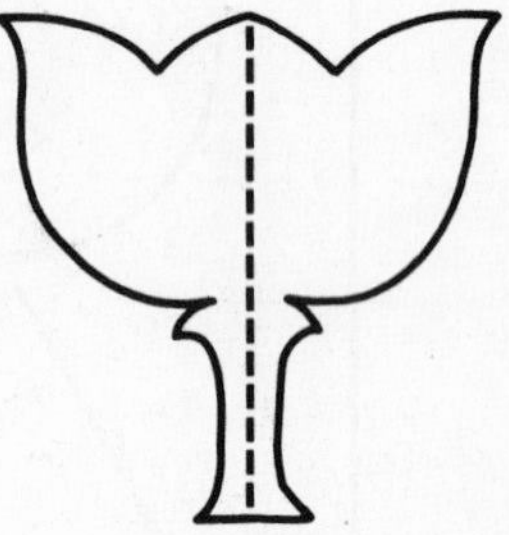

7. 

8. 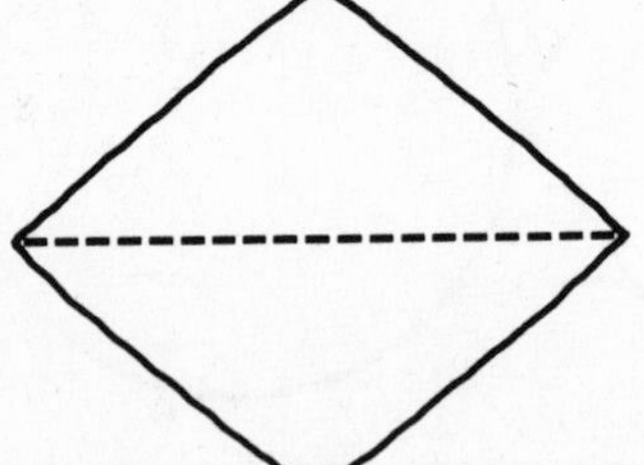

9. 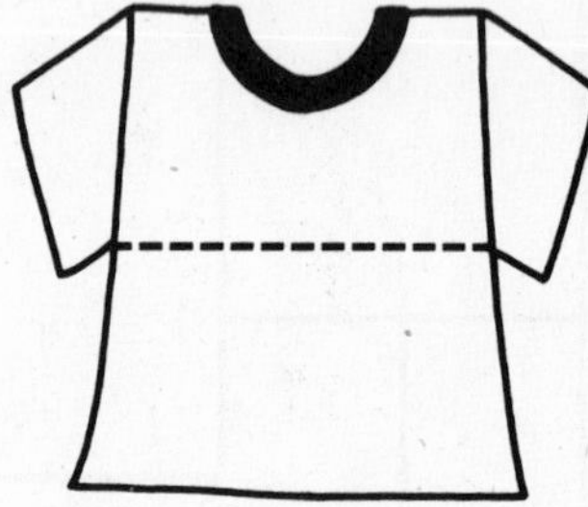

10. 

11. 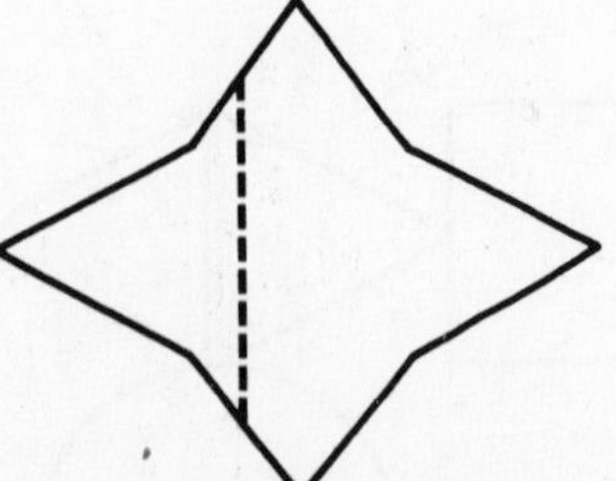

12. 

Name

PROBLEM SOLVING STRATEGY: FINDING A PATTERN

Color to show the pattern.

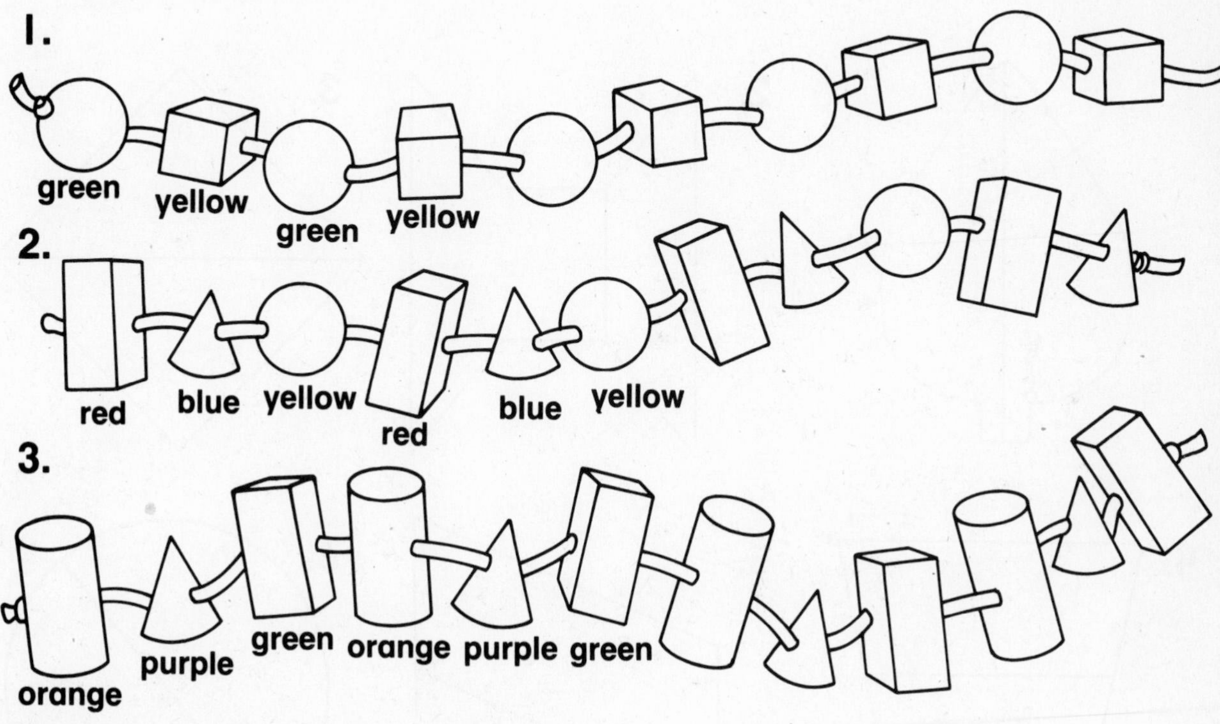

Make up your own patterns.

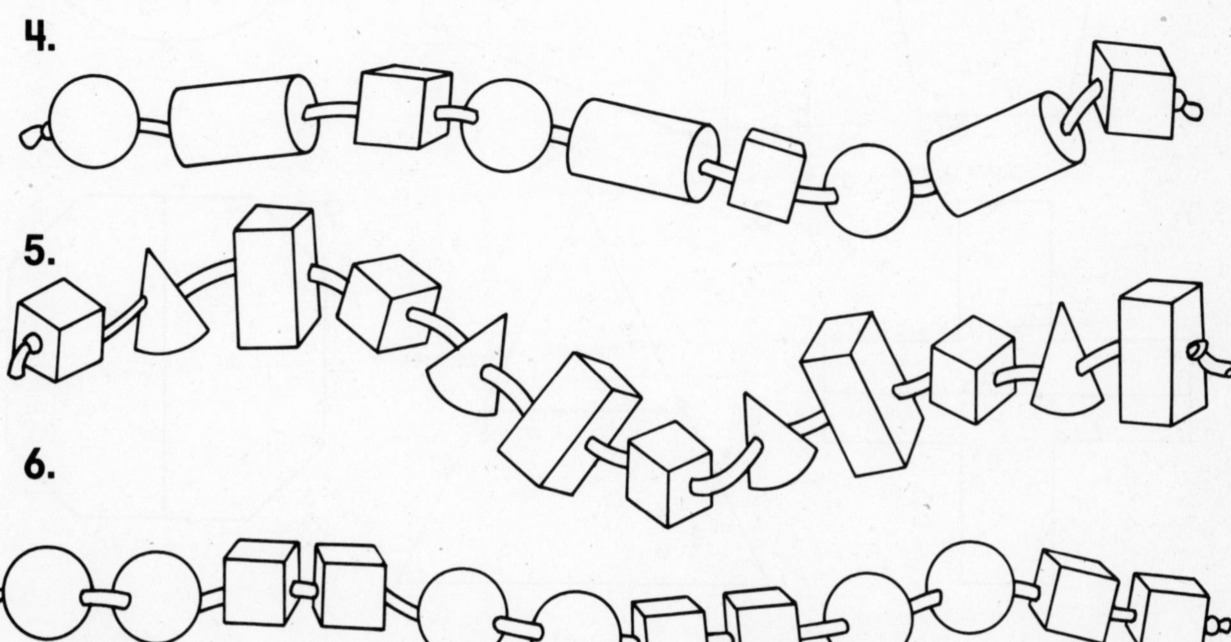

Name

HALVES

Color $\frac{1}{2}$.
Do not color if the shape does not show halves.

1.
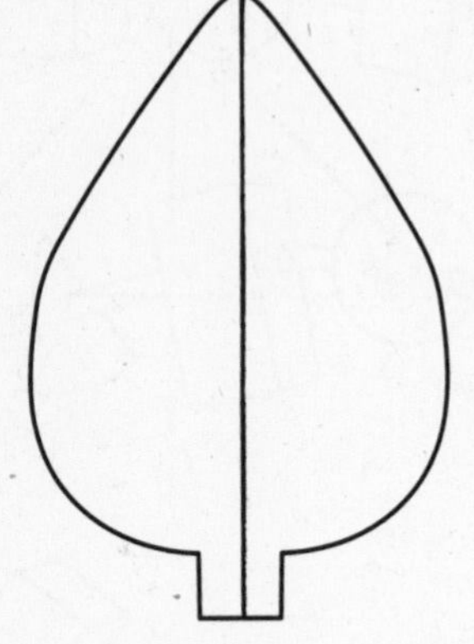

2.
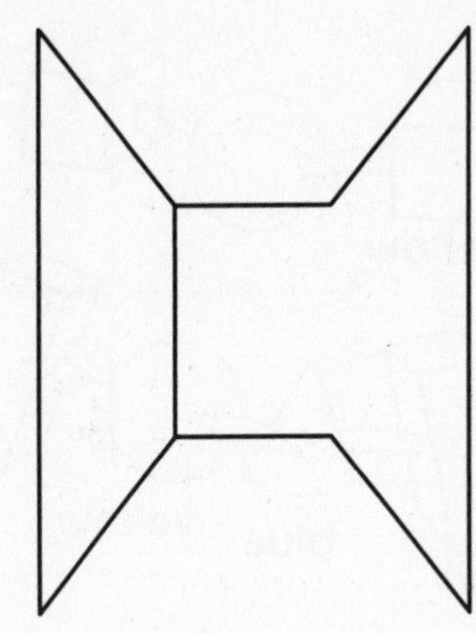

3.
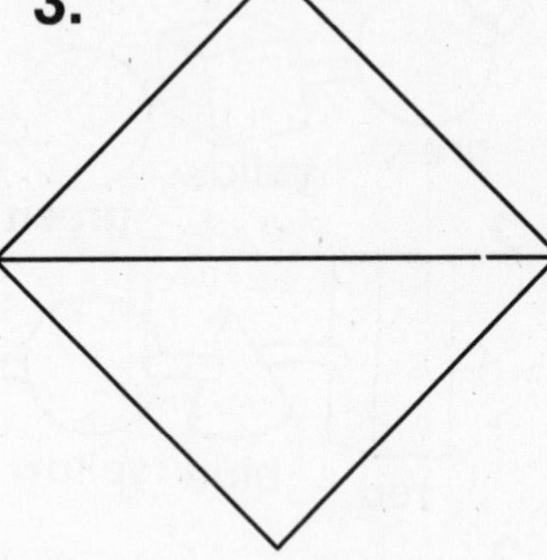

4.
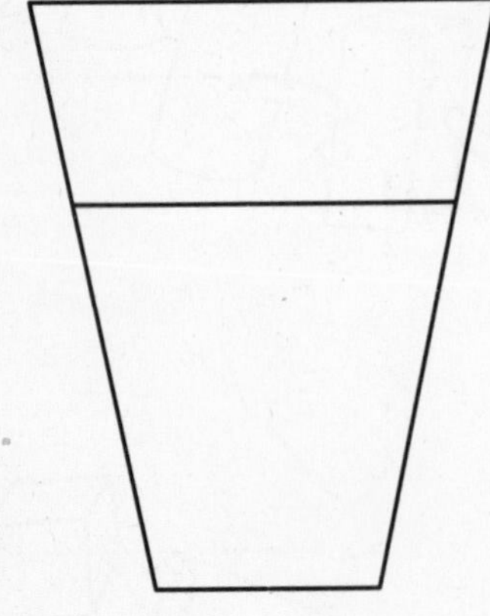

5.
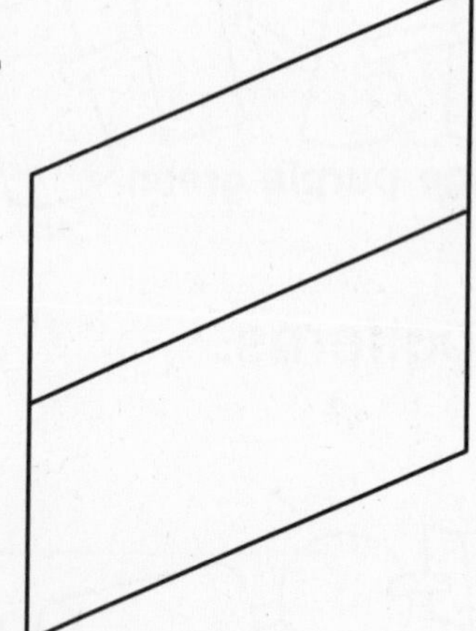

6.
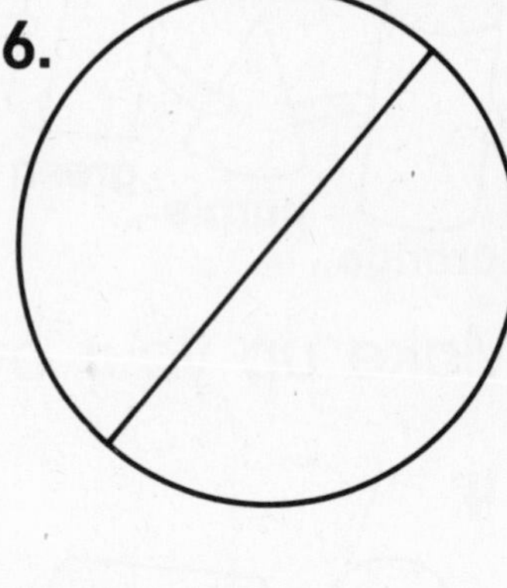

7.
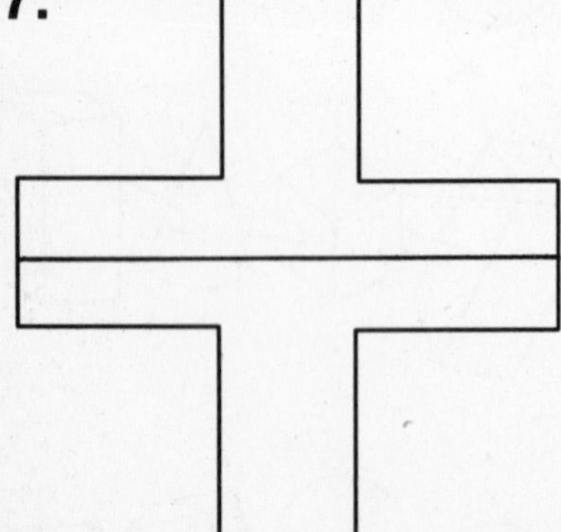

8.

9.
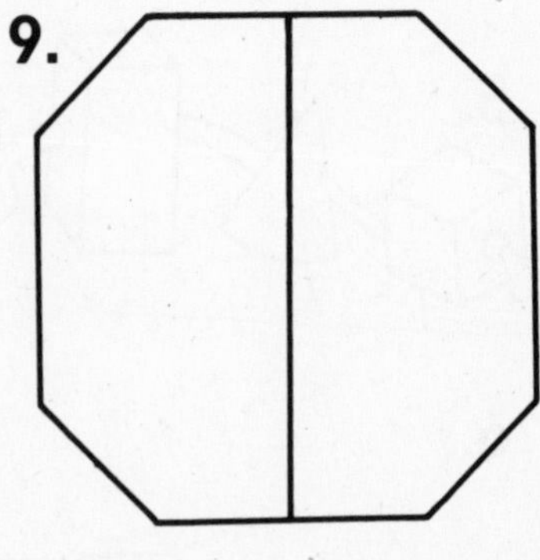

Name

FOURTHS

Color $\frac{1}{4}$.
Do not color if the shape does not show fourths.

1. 

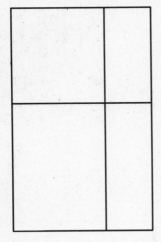

2. 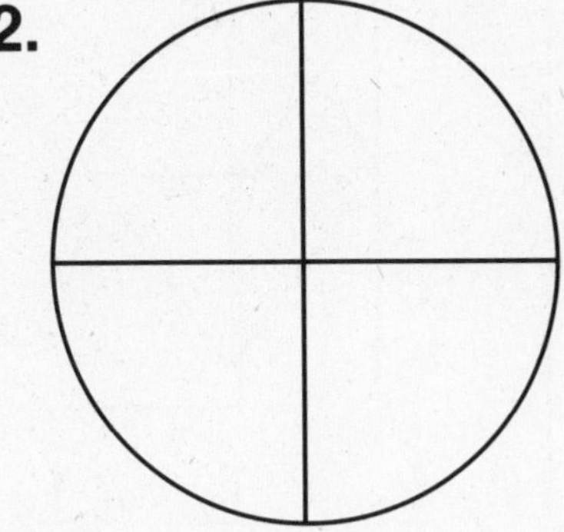

3. 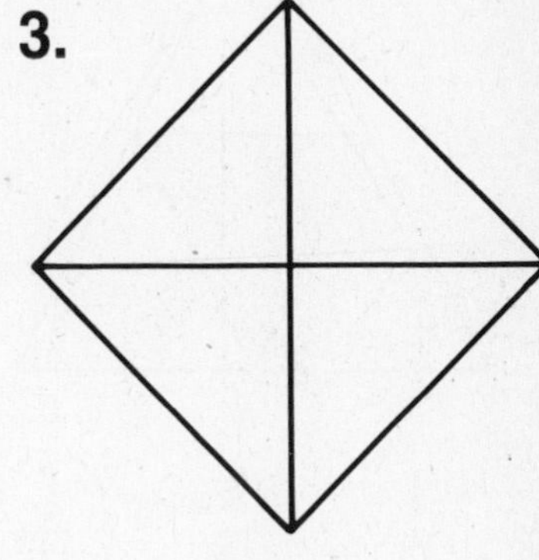

4. 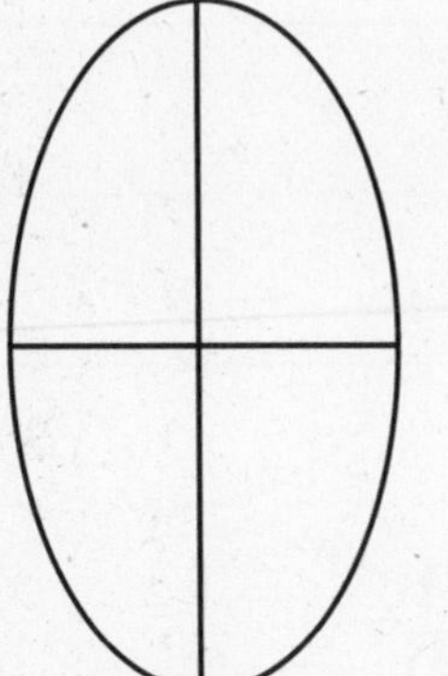

5. 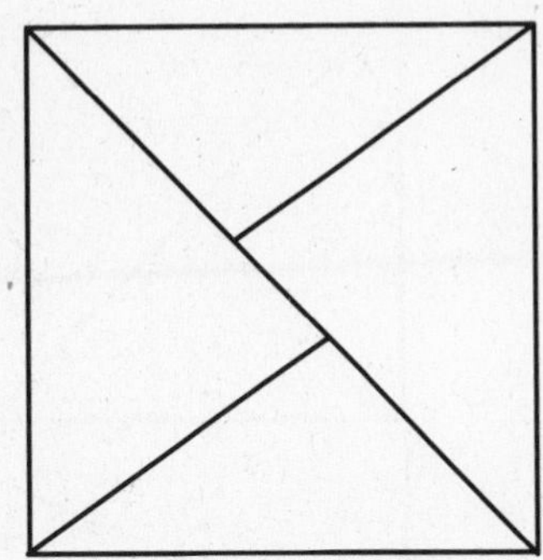

6. 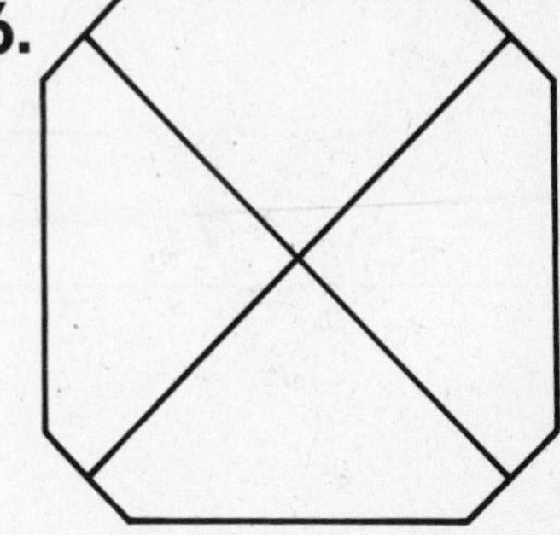

7. 

8. 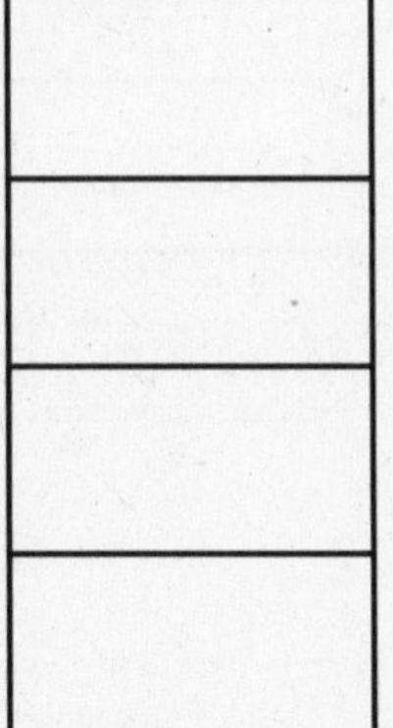

9. 

Macmillan/McGraw-Hill, MATHEMATICS IN ACTION
Grade 1, Chapter 11, Lesson 8, pages 335–336

Name

THIRDS

Ring the fraction.

1.

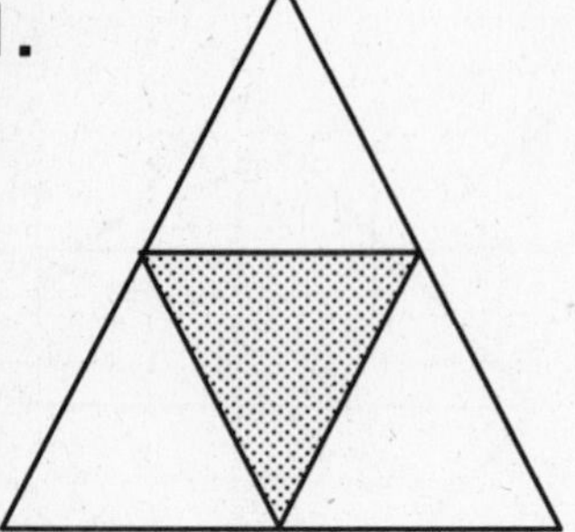

$\frac{1}{2}$ $\frac{1}{3}$ $\frac{1}{4}$

2.

$\frac{1}{2}$ $\frac{1}{3}$ $\frac{1}{4}$

3.

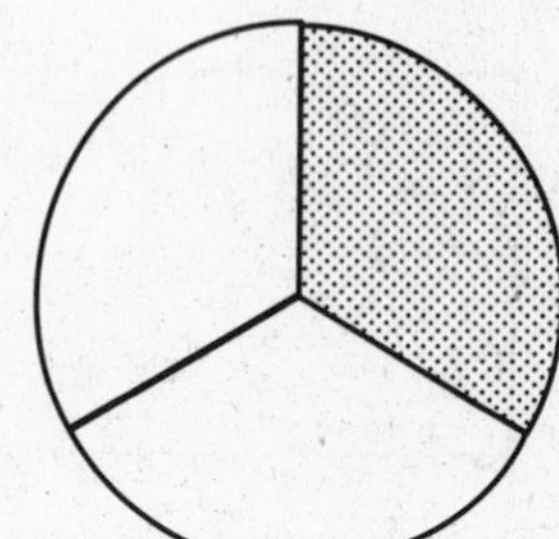

$\frac{1}{2}$ $\frac{1}{3}$ $\frac{1}{4}$

4.

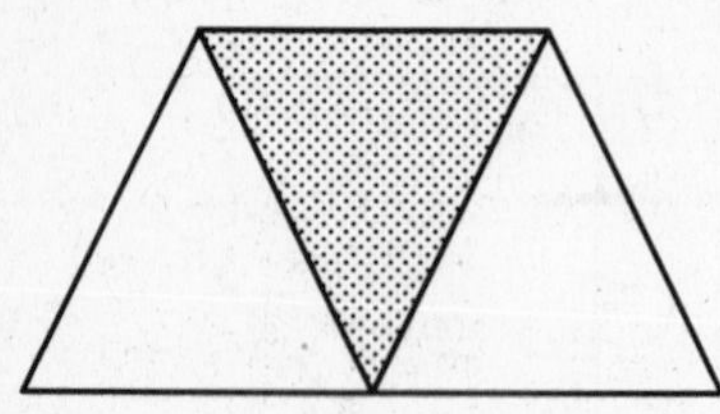

$\frac{1}{2}$ $\frac{1}{3}$ $\frac{1}{4}$

5.

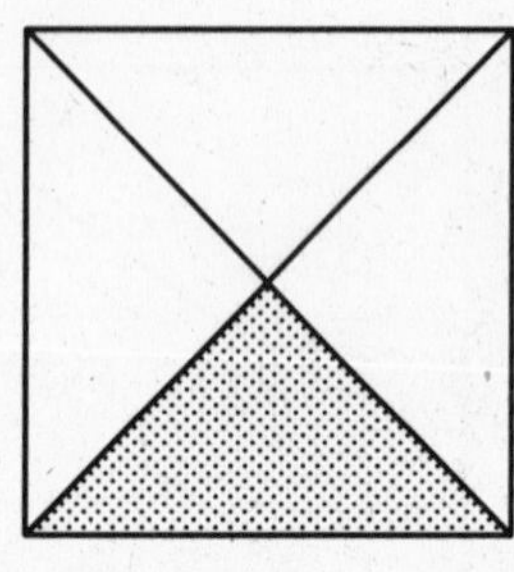

$\frac{1}{2}$ $\frac{1}{3}$ $\frac{1}{4}$

6.

$\frac{1}{2}$ $\frac{1}{3}$ $\frac{1}{4}$

7.

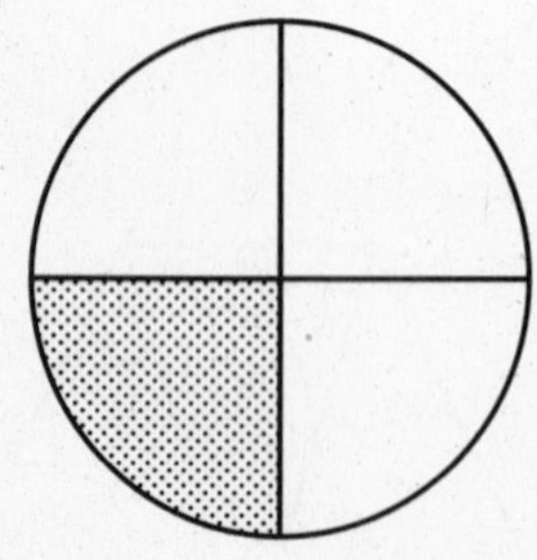

$\frac{1}{2}$ $\frac{1}{3}$ $\frac{1}{4}$

8.

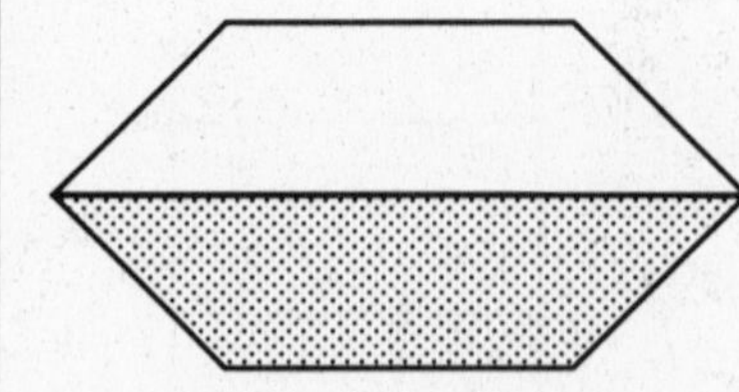

$\frac{1}{2}$ $\frac{1}{3}$ $\frac{1}{4}$

9.

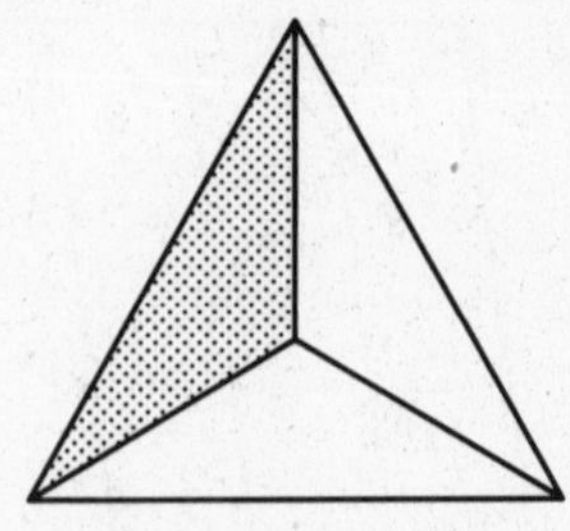

$\frac{1}{2}$ $\frac{1}{3}$ $\frac{1}{4}$

Name

PROBLEM SOLVING STRATEGY: DRAWING A PICTURE

Draw a picture to show how the children share.

1.  2 children share the piece of pie.

2.  4 children share the sandwich.

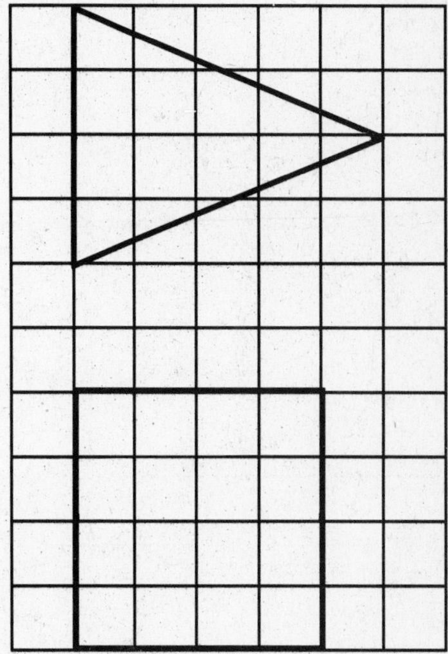

Ring the pictures to show how the children share.

3. There are 6 apples. 2 children share.

4. There are 8 oranges. 4 children share.

 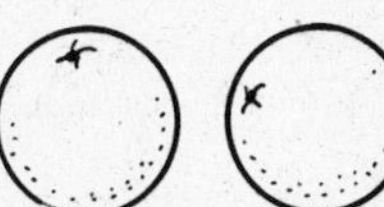    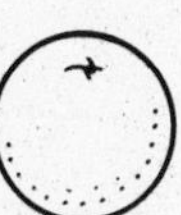 

5. There are 6 pears. 3 children share.

Name

SUMS AND DIFFERENCES TO 13

Write an addition fact and a subtraction fact.

1. 6 + 7 = 13 13 − 7 = 6

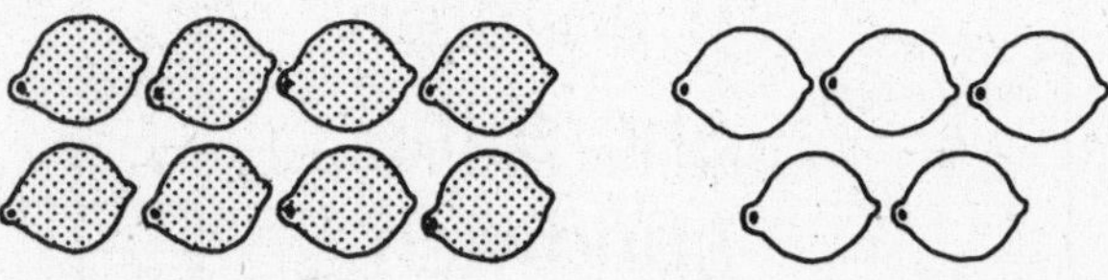

2. _____ + _____ = _____ _____ − _____ = _____

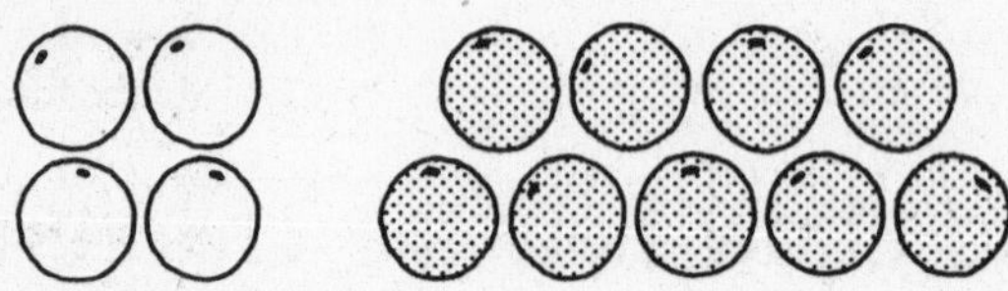

3. _____ + _____ = _____ _____ − _____ = _____

4. _____ + _____ = _____ _____ − _____ = _____

5. _____ + _____ = _____ _____ − _____ = _____

Name

MORE SUMS AND DIFFERENCES TO 13

Write the fact family.

1. 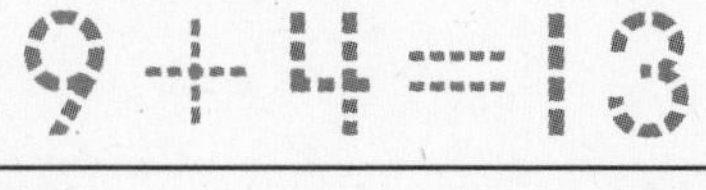
9 + 4 = 13 13 − 4 = 9
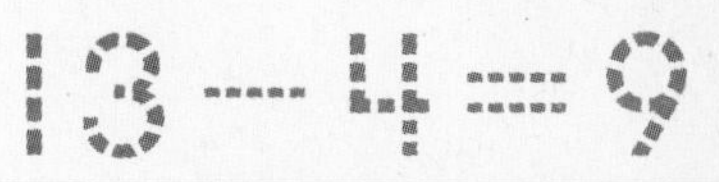
4 + 9 = 13 13 − 9 = 4
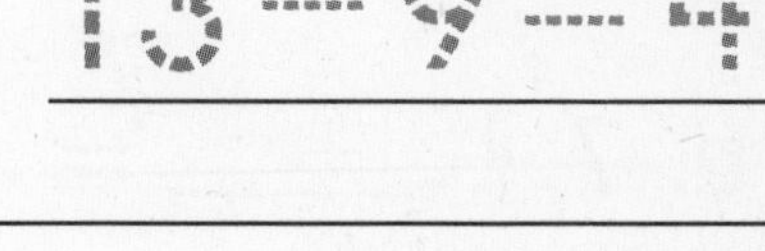

2.

3.

4.

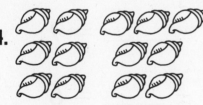

5.

Macmillan/McGraw-Hill, MATHEMATICS IN ACTION
Grade 1, Chapter 12, Lesson 3, pages 357–358

Name ______

SUMS AND DIFFERENCES TO 14

Use cubes to find the missing numbers.

1. 5 + 9 = 14   14 − ____ = 5
2. 7 + ____ = 14   14 − ____ = 7
3. 7 + ____ = 12   12 − ____ = 7
4. 8 + ____ = 14   14 − ____ = 8
5. 6 + ____ = 11   11 − ____ = 6
6. 8 + ____ = 12   12 − ____ = 8
7. 9 + ____ = 14   14 − ____ = 9
8. 9 + ____ = 13   13 − ____ = 9
9. 6 + ____ = 14   14 − ____ = 6
10. 3 + ____ = 12   12 − ____ = 3
11. 7 + ____ = 9   9 − ____ = 7
12. 6 + ____ = 12   12 − ____ = 6

Name

More sums and differences to 14

CODE

F	Y	K	S	R	E	A	C	W	O	N
4	5	6	7	8	9	10	11	12	13	14

Add or subtract.
Write the missing letters.

7 + 5 = 12 W, H, 2 + 8, T, 12 − 6, I, 6 + 8, D

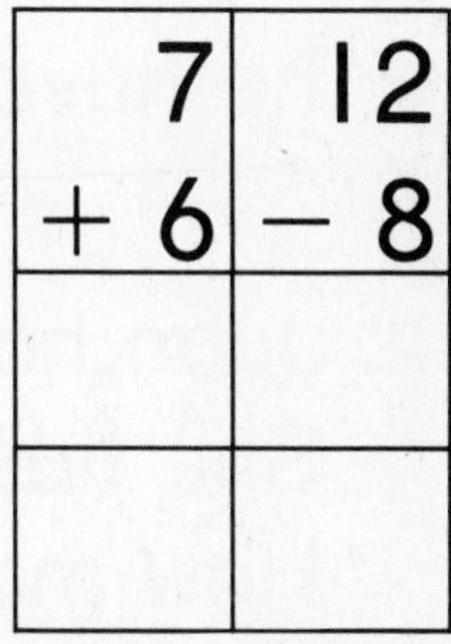

7 + 6, 12 − 8

6 + 5, 14 − 6, 5 + 8, 6 + 6

7 + 4, 3 + 7, 7 + 7

5 + 9, 9 + 4 T

13 − 9 L

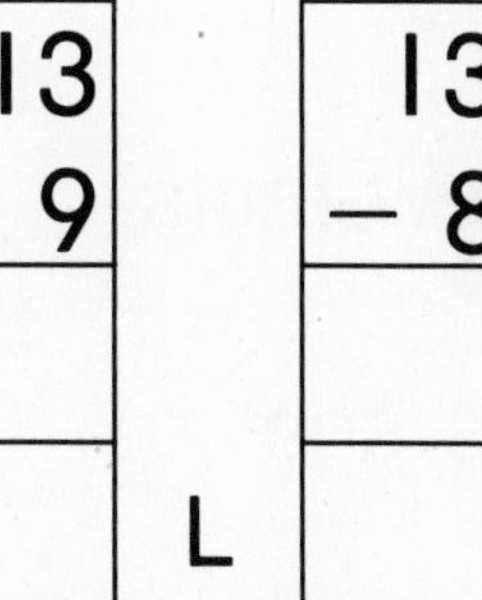

13 − 8 ?

5 + 5

14 − 7, 8 + 3, 6 + 4, 12 − 4, 14 − 5, 2 + 9, 13 − 5, 4 + 9, 8 + 4

Name

PROBLEM SOLVING STRATEGY: CHOOSING THE OPERATION

Solve.

1. Greg has 12 stamps.
He put 8 stamps on cards.
How many stamps does
he have left? 4 stamps

2. Joan has 8 cookies.
She has 5 muffins.
How many more cookies than
muffins does she have? ______ more

3. Mark has 6 balloons.
Marie has 9 balloons.
How many balloons do they
have in all? ______ balloons

4. Sandra learned 12 new facts.
She forgot 3 facts.
How many facts does she
remember? ______ facts

5. Sally made 8 kites on
Monday.
She made 6 kites on Tuesday.
How many kites did she
make in the two days? ______ kites

Name ______________________________

SUMS AND DIFFERENCES TO 15

Add or subtract.

1.	4 + 9 13	7 + 7	8 + 3		
2.	15 − 8 7	13 − 7	14 − 5	12 − 5	14 − 8
3.	9 + 6	12 − 8	6 + 8	15 − 9	13 − 9
4.	14 − 9	5 + 9	13 − 6	14 − 7	7 + 8
5.	8 + 5	15 − 7	6 + 9	13 − 8	9 + 4
6.	14 − 6	9 + 5	15 − 6	8 + 6	8 + 7

Macmillan/McGraw-Hill, MATHEMATICS IN ACTION
Grade 1, Chapter 12, Lesson 8, pages 367–368

Name

SUMS AND DIFFERENCES TO 16, 17, AND 18

Add or subtract.

1. $\begin{array}{r}14\\-\ 8\\\hline 6\end{array}$ $\begin{array}{r}9\\+6\\\hline\end{array}$ $\begin{array}{r}8\\+8\\\hline\end{array}$ $\begin{array}{r}16\\-\ 9\\\hline\end{array}$

2. $\begin{array}{r}18\\-\ 9\\\hline\end{array}$ $\begin{array}{r}5\\+9\\\hline\end{array}$ $\begin{array}{r}15\\-\ 9\\\hline\end{array}$ $\begin{array}{r}7\\+7\\\hline\end{array}$ $\begin{array}{r}13\\-\ 4\\\hline\end{array}$ $\begin{array}{r}9\\+8\\\hline\end{array}$ $\begin{array}{r}12\\-\ 8\\\hline\end{array}$

3. $\begin{array}{r}15\\-\ 6\\\hline\end{array}$ $\begin{array}{r}13\\-\ 5\\\hline\end{array}$ $\begin{array}{r}8\\+9\\\hline\end{array}$ $\begin{array}{r}14\\-\ 9\\\hline\end{array}$ $\begin{array}{r}8\\+6\\\hline\end{array}$ $\begin{array}{r}16\\-\ 8\\\hline\end{array}$ $\begin{array}{r}7\\+8\\\hline\end{array}$

4. $\begin{array}{r}9\\+7\\\hline\end{array}$ $\begin{array}{r}12\\-\ 7\\\hline\end{array}$ $\begin{array}{r}17\\-\ 9\\\hline\end{array}$ $\begin{array}{r}6\\+9\\\hline\end{array}$ $\begin{array}{r}14\\-\ 7\\\hline\end{array}$ $\begin{array}{r}9\\+4\\\hline\end{array}$ $\begin{array}{r}15\\-\ 8\\\hline\end{array}$

5. $\begin{array}{r}14\\-\ 5\\\hline\end{array}$ $\begin{array}{r}13\\-\ 8\\\hline\end{array}$ $\begin{array}{r}9\\+9\\\hline\end{array}$ $\begin{array}{r}15\\-\ 7\\\hline\end{array}$ $\begin{array}{r}5\\+8\\\hline\end{array}$ $\begin{array}{r}13\\-\ 6\\\hline\end{array}$ $\begin{array}{r}7\\+9\\\hline\end{array}$

6. $\begin{array}{r}9\\+5\\\hline\end{array}$ $\begin{array}{r}16\\-\ 7\\\hline\end{array}$ $\begin{array}{r}8\\+7\\\hline\end{array}$ $\begin{array}{r}14\\-\ 6\\\hline\end{array}$ $\begin{array}{r}12\\-\ 9\\\hline\end{array}$ $\begin{array}{r}17\\-\ 8\\\hline\end{array}$ $\begin{array}{r}6\\+8\\\hline\end{array}$

Macmillan/McGraw-Hill, MATHEMATICS IN ACTION
Grade 1, Chapter 12, Lesson 9, pages 369–370

MACMILLAN/McGRAW-HILL.

Name

ADDITION AND SUBTRACTION PATTERNS

Add or subtract.

1.						
	18	17	16	15	14	13
	− 9	− 9	− 9	− 9	− 9	− 9
	9					

2.						
	4	5	6	7	8	9
	+ 2	+ 2	+ 2	+ 2	+ 2	+ 2

3.						
	13	13	13	13	13	13
	− 4	− 5	− 6	− 7	− 8	− 9

4.						
	4	5	6	7	8	9
	+ 4	+ 5	+ 6	+ 7	+ 8	+ 9

5.						
	13	14	15	16	17	18
	− 4	− 5	− 6	− 7	− 8	− 9

6.						
	3	4	5	6	7	8
	+ 4	+ 5	+ 6	+ 7	+ 8	+ 9

Name

MONEY

Add or subtract.

1. 8¢ + 7¢ = 15¢   9¢ + 9¢   7¢ + 5¢   8¢ + 8¢   9¢ + 6¢

2. 16¢ − 7¢   14¢ − 8¢   18¢ − 9¢   13¢ − 8¢   15¢ − 7¢

3. 9¢ + 8¢   8¢ + 5¢   7¢ + 9¢   9¢ + 4¢   6¢ + 7¢

4. 15¢ − 6¢   16¢ − 8¢   12¢ − 7¢   17¢ − 8¢   14¢ − 5¢

Solve.

5. You have 17¢.
You spend 9¢.
How much money
do you have left?

______

6. 7¢ for a pencil.
6¢ for a pad.
How much money
in all?

______

Name

Adding Three Numbers

Add to complete each wheel.

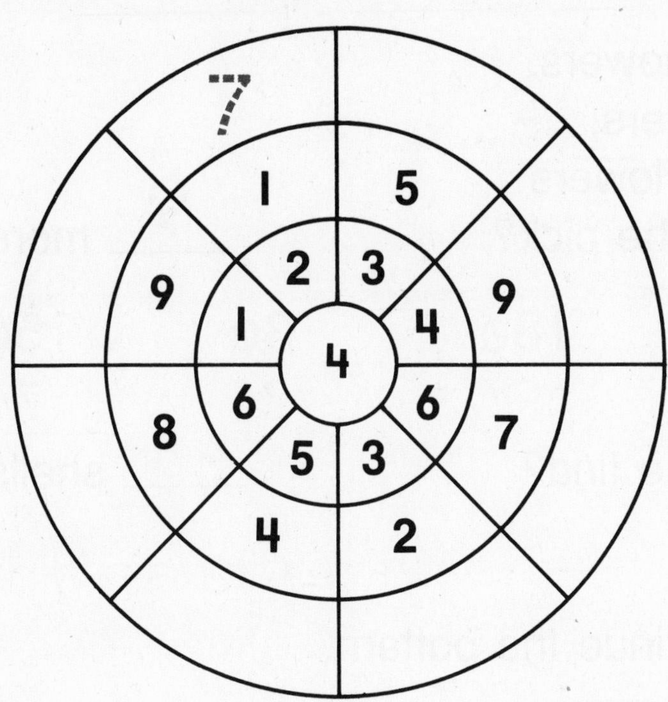

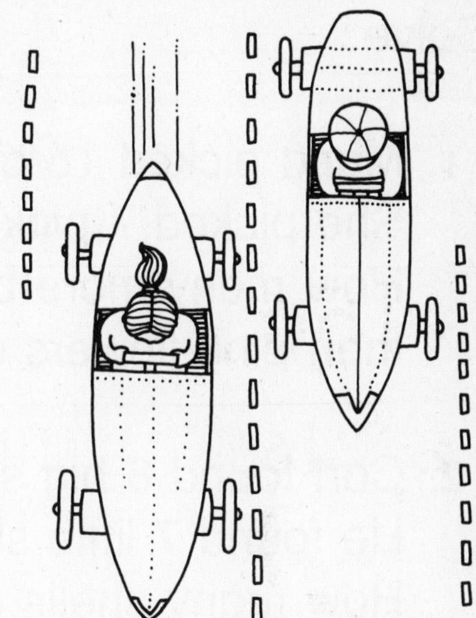

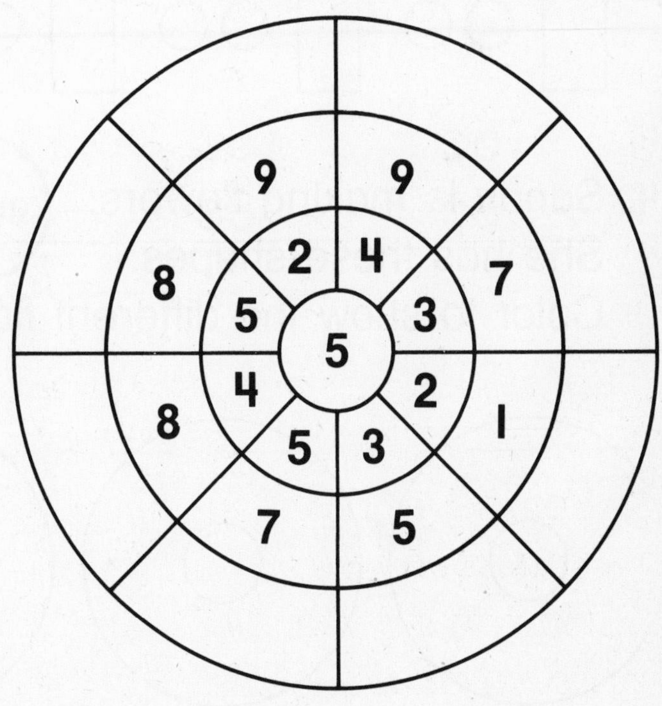

Name

PROBLEM SOLVING STRATEGIES REVIEW

Solve.

1. Maria picked 16 blue flowers.
   She picked 7 pink flowers.
   How many more blue flowers
   than pink flowers did she pick?  ______ more

2. Carl found 8 big shells.
   He found 7 little shells.
   How many shells did he find? ______ shells

3. Look for a pattern.
   Ring the shape to continue the pattern.

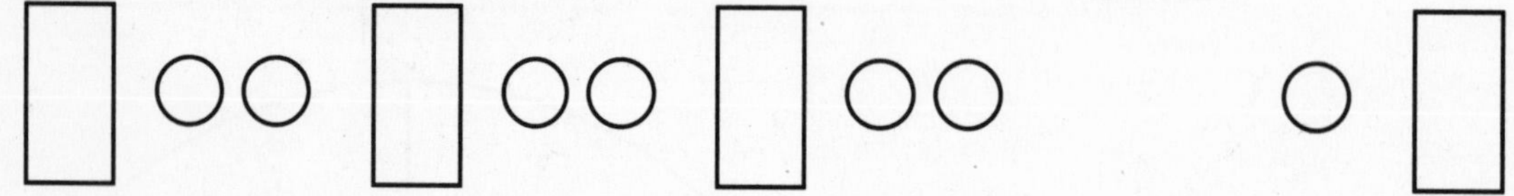

4. Sandy is making flowers.
   She has these shapes.
   Color to show the different flowers.

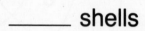

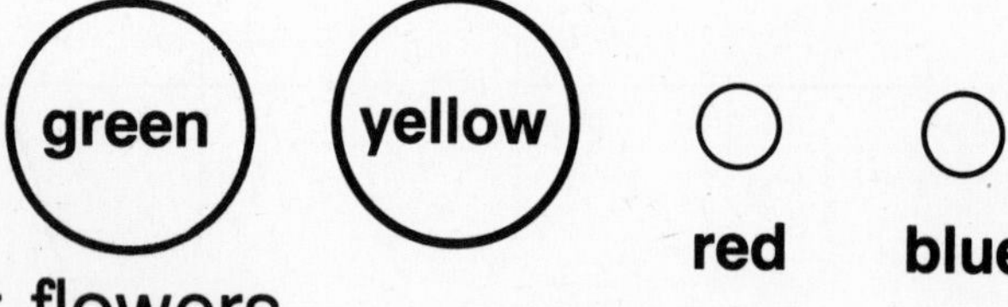

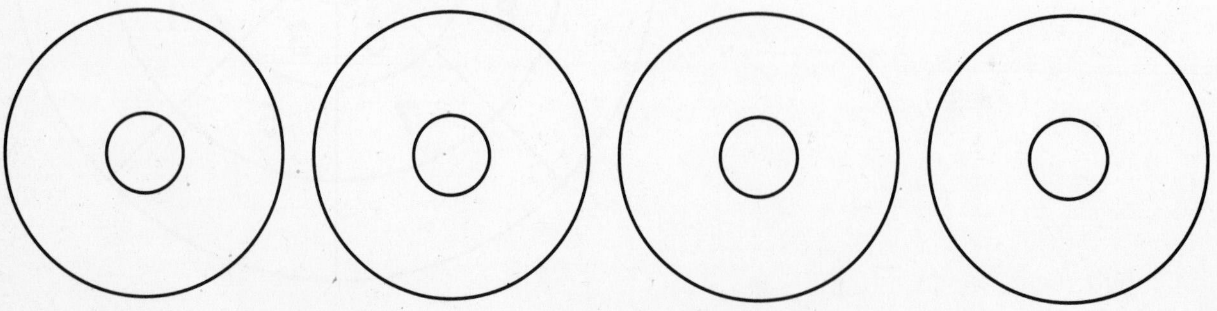

She can make ______ different flowers.

Name

PROBLEM SOLVING STRATEGY: USING INFORMATION FROM A TABLE

The teams run on Saturday and Sunday. The table shows how many miles each team ran last year.

MILES RUN

	Saturday	Sunday
Bees	22	16
Reds	15	21
Hawks	32	12
Stars	24	13

Write the numbers. Solve.

1. The Bees ran _____ miles on Saturday.

   They ran _____ miles on Sunday.
   How many miles did they run on both days? _____

2. The Hawks ran _____ miles on Sunday.

   They ran _____ miles on Saturday.
   How many miles did they run on both days? _____

3. The Reds ran _____ miles on Saturday.

   The Stars ran _____ miles on Saturday.
   How many miles did they run on Saturday? _____

4. The Stars ran _____ miles on Sunday.

   The Hawks ran _____ miles on Sunday.
   How many miles did they run on Sunday? _____

Macmillan/McGraw-Hill, MATHEMATICS IN ACTION
Grade 1, Chapter 13, Lesson 4, pages 393–394

Name

SUBTRACTING ONES AND TENS

Use Workmat 3. Use 9 ▭ and 7 ▭▭▭▭▭▭▭▭▭▭.
Find the difference.

1.

	tens	ones		tens	ones		tens	ones		tens	ones
	6	9		3	7		7	6		4	8
−		5	−		6	−		5	−		2
	6	4									

2.

	tens	ones		tens	ones		tens	ones		tens	ones
	2	5		5	4		6	8		7	9
−		3	−		1	−		4	−		4

3.

	tens	ones		tens	ones		tens	ones		tens	ones
	4	7		3	5		5	6		2	4
−		5	−		4	−		4	−		2

4.

	tens	ones		tens	ones		tens	ones		tens	ones
	6	7		5	8		7	5		4	9
−		4	−		6	−		2	−		3

Name ______________________________

MORE SUBTRACTING ONES AND TENS

Subtract.

1.

	tens	ones
	8	6
−	6	4
	2	2

	tens	ones
	5	8
−	1	4

	tens	ones
	9	5
−	7	5

	tens	ones
	6	7
−	5	6

2.

	tens	ones
	3	9
−	1	6

	tens	ones
	7	2
−	3	2

	tens	ones
	2	3
−	1	2

	tens	ones
	4	4
−	1	3

3. 97 − 34 = ___ 78 − 35 = ___ 59 − 38 = ___ 85 − 32 = ___ 46 − 23 = ___

4. 34 − 24 = ___ 63 − 11 = ___ 22 − 10 = ___ 98 − 18 = ___ 79 − 54 = ___

5. 65 − 34 = ___ 84 − 73 = ___ 43 − 10 = ___ 56 − 12 = ___ 37 − 34 = ___

Macmillan/McGraw-Hill, MATHEMATICS IN ACTION
Grade 1, Chapter 13, Lesson 7, pages 399–400

Name

ADDING AND SUBTRACTING MONEY

Add or subtract.

1.

20¢	33¢	50¢	18¢	21¢
+ 8¢	+ 11¢	+ 30¢	+ 10¢	+ 42¢
28¢				

2.

13¢	74¢	53¢	14¢	25¢
+ 6¢	+ 12¢	+ 16¢	+ 61¢	+ 3¢

3.

79¢	54¢	98¢	67¢	35¢
− 65¢	− 22¢	− 7¢	− 14¢	− 30¢
14¢				

4.

29¢	88¢	95¢	56¢	47¢
− 17¢	− 55¢	− 33¢	− 6¢	− 12¢

Solve.

5. Terry had 75¢
She spent 23¢.
How much money
does she have left?

______

6. Lew bought a toy for
15¢. He bought a book
for 30¢. How much did
he spend in all?

______

Name

PROBLEM SOLVING STRATEGY: USING ESTIMATION

Ring the closer estimate.

1. Tony made 17 cookies. Sue made 21 cookies. About how many cookies did they make?

   30 cookies
   40 cookies

2. Tina planted 21 daisies. She planted 12 tulips. About how many flowers did she plant?

   30 flowers
   40 flowers

3. Connie read 32 pages today. She read 18 pages yesterday. About how many more pages did she read today?

   10 pages
   20 pages

4. Sam put 41 fish in his new tank. He has 23 fish in his old tank. About how many more fish does Sam have in his new tank?

   10 fish
   20 fish

5. Betty sewed 19 beads on her dress. She sewed 18 beads on her hat. About how many beads did she sew?

   20 beads
   40 beads

Macmillan/McGraw-Hill, MATHEMATICS IN ACTION
Grade 1, Chapter 13, Lesson 12, pages 409–410